ANZA
Hard-Riding Captain

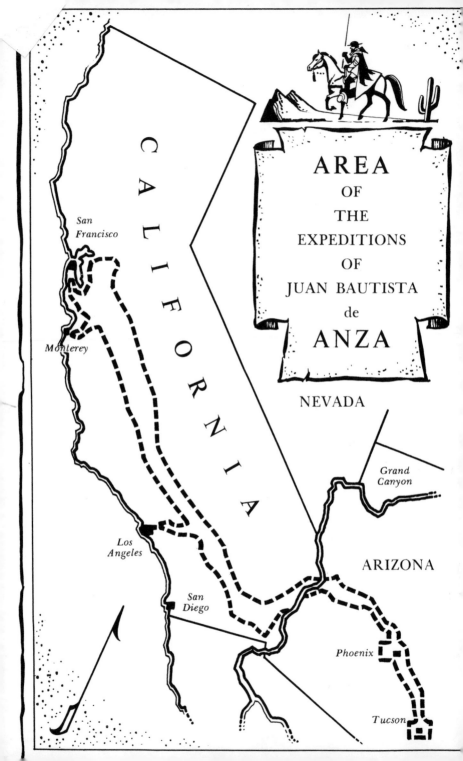

AREA
OF
THE
EXPEDITIONS
OF
JUAN BAUTISTA
de
ANZA

CALIFORNIA

San Francisco

Monterey

Los Angeles

San Diego

NEVADA

Grand Canyon

ARIZONA

Phoenix

Tucson

ANZA

Hard-Riding Captain

BOB and JAN YOUNG

GOLDEN GATE JUNIOR BOOKS

San Carlos • California

To ALEC, HARRELL *and* DON
*without whom this book would not
have been possible*

Foreword

In the 1770's, while the Thirteen Colonies were writing their Declaration of Independence in blood, another significant struggle was taking place on the Pacific Coast.

Following Columbus's discovery of the New World, Spain had built a powerful colonial empire in Mexico and South America. As early as the days of Cortez, ships sailing west into the Pacific Ocean had reached Lower California. In 1542 the explorer Cabrillo had entered San Diego Bay to make the first landing in Alta California. However, for nearly two centuries the Spaniards made no effort to occupy this new land, although their great Manila galleons stopped along the coast occasionally to take on water on their return from the Philippines.

Then, in the eighteenth century, Spain's position as the dominant power in the New World began to fade. To the north of her, on the Atlantic coast, the English colonies were firmly entrenched and prospering. On the Pacific Coast the Russians, led by Vitus Bering, had reached Alaska. In 1769 Spain sent an expedition, led by Portolá and Father Junípero Serra, to found a slim chain of presidios and missions along the California coast. Unlike the English, who settled a new land by sending colonists, for centuries Spain had advanced her frontiers by soldier and priest. With the small, often-delayed ships that battled their way up the coast of Mexico their only source of supplies, these men of the new California settlements lived constantly on the verge of starvation. If Spain was to keep her foothold in this new land it was evident she too must send permanent settlers; men, women and children to build homes and to till the soil. She must also send cattle herds to support them and find some overland route to keep her settlements supplied.

Unfortunately, no such route was known. Although the Mexican frontier had been moved north to what is today the lower edge of Arizona, early explorers said it was impossible to go farther northwest because of a "terrible desert" that separated Mexico from California.

Juan Bautista de Anza, a courageous frontier soldier, was chosen by Destiny to lead the way. It was Anza who found a route across the desert and later brought the first colonists to establish the city of San Francisco. That he also distinguished himself as Governor of New Mexico and Mexico's foremost Indian fighter were only sidelights on this hard-riding captain's remarkable career.

The authors wish to express their thanks to Doctor Andrew F. Rolle, Professor of History, Occidental College, for reading the manuscript.

Bob and Jan Young
March, 1966   *Whittier, California*

Contents

Beginning Of A Dream

"ALTO! WHO GOES THERE?" The sharp command shattered the quiet desert air.

From the sun-baked grazing lands beyond the walls of the adobe fort there was only silence. Not even a rustling breeze betrayed the source of the warning crackle which had startled the sentry. But in the 1740's at Fronteras, one of the northernmost presidios on the Mexican border, guards were always alert.

"Halt! Show yourself!" The soldier raised his musket.

There was a faint stirring behind a distant clump of brush. Instead of a dreaded Apache, a stocky, black-haired boy of twelve rose sheepishly. "It is only I, Juan."

"So it's you again! How many times have you been warned—" The soldier lowered the gun. "If you must play soldier and Indian, can't you stay inside the fort?"

The boy drew himself up haughtily. "I wasn't hunting Indians. I was exploring." He pointed northwest to the blue mountains that fringed the desert. "See that pass? Someday I shall see what lies beyond those hills. Someday I shall go west across the big river and the terrible desert to the new land they call California."

"California!" snorted the sentry. "Before you'd gone twenty leagues, the savages would have you. We have more important things to do than to dream of what lies beyond the mountains. Unless you learn to respect the Apaches you'll not grow up to carry a musket."

"I give the Apaches credit, sir," the boy replied. Struggling free from the soldier's restraining arm, his face cracked in a impudent grin. "But they don't scare me into challenging twelve-year-old boys and every rustle in the dry leaves!"

"Big talk for a little man!" the red-faced soldier bellowed after the retreating figure. "Someday you'll regret those words, Juan Bautista de Anza!"

"Little man indeed!" Young Juan scuffed angrily at the thick yellow dust of the plaza. At twelve he was already as strong as some grown men. It was only because his widowed mother considered him too young that he was not serving as a soldier already. But someday he would show them. Someday he would find what lay beyond those hills!

Even here, at the remote frontier forts along the Sonoran border, the people had heard of the land called California which lay to the north of Mexico. Every schoolboy knew of the exploits of Cermeño, Viscaíno, and Cabrillo, the sea captains who had sailed their ships along the California coast. Now, travelers brought stories of Father Kino who, journeying as far north as the Colorado River, had discovered that California was not an island, as everyone had once believed, but was actually connected to Mexico by a great impassable desert which lay beyond the river.

Young Juan's dream was not an original one. His father, once presidio captain at Fronteras, had cherished the same dream. He had even been granted permission to make an expedition. But before he was able to set out he had been killed in battle with the Apaches. Young Juan would have done well to have paid more attention to the sentry's warning. The same Indians who had destroyed his father's plans were to delay his own ambitions for twenty-five long years.

The twenty-five years were not idle ones. Born in Fronteras in 1735, Juan Bautista de Anza belonged to the frontier aristocracy. For thirty years his grandfather had been presidio captain at Janos. His father had served another thirty years at Fronteras. At eighteen, following family tradition, young Anza finally joined the army. By twenty he had been promoted to captain. With another young officer, he immediately petitioned the Governor of Sonora for permission to lead his first exploration party, but an Indian uprising changed their plans. After that came more years of Indian fighting against Apaches, Seris, and Pimas. By the time he was twenty-five Anza had been rewarded for his bravery with the command of his own presidio at Tubac.

Northwest of Fronteras, across the border in what is now Arizona, Tubac was the last jumping-off place into the unknown land to the north. But again Anza's dreams of exploration were lost in the rigorous demands of his work.

The soldiers who served on the frontier were a tough, hardened lot. They were required to take part of their pay in supplies and many a presidio captain built a private fortune by charging exorbitant prices. Upon his arrival at Tubac, Anza immediately lowered prices. This not only won him the respect of his men but as news of his fairness spread, settlers flocked from other presidios to live at Tubac. Among the newcomers was the young and beautiful Doña Ana de Serrano, sister of the post chaplain, who became Anza's wife.

Anza's reputation for personal courage brought him even more renown. Soon he was recognized as the leading Indian fighter on the border. He led new expeditions against the Apaches and Seris and brought the entire tribe of Pápagos into submission by defeating their chief in hand-to-hand combat.

While Anza was defending the northern border, in the capital at Mexico City interest in the new land of California was increasing. Captains of returning Manila galleons, who stopped along the coast to take on water, told fabulous tales of fertile California valleys and thousands of Indians waiting to accept Christianity. Finally, in 1769, Portolá, accompanied by Father Junípero Serra, led the first expedition to found the presidios of San Diego and Monterey and start the first missions.

Months later, in his quarters at Tubac, Anza was busily preparing reports for an expected visit from José de Gálvez, Inspector General of Spain, when he was interrupted by a messenger. The soldier saluted. "I wish to report the capture of a Pima Indian, sir."

"And what is so important about a Pima Indian?" It was impossible for Anza to hide his annoyance at being interrupted. After fighting Pimas for twenty years, one more didn't impress him.

"This is no ordinary Pima, sir," the soldier persisted. "He is not one of the neophytes from the missions of the Altar Valley. He comes from a tribe to the north along the Gila River."

"Pimas, Pápagos, Seris!" Anza muttered disgustedly, pushing·back his papers.

Beyond the doorway of the squat adobe building the sunlight was blinding. But by the time he had walked halfway across the hard-packed square, Anza's eyes had accustomed themselves sufficiently to the glare so that he could see, to his disgust, that the Indian waiting for him looked no different than any other Pima. Like his fellow tribesmen, he was of stocky build, very dark-skinned, and he wore the usual woven blanket twisted into a rough semblance of a pair of breeches. On his head was a fiber band into which had been stuck decorative twigs and a feather. Any fear he might have felt in the presence of so many soldiers had been forgotten in his delight at being the center of attention.

"He brings a strange story, Captain," one of the soldiers said. "That is, if he hasn't made it up just to wheedle us out of some gifts."

Motioning the soldier to silence, Anza turned to the Indian. "What is this great tale you bear?"

With many gestures, accompanied by rough, guttural language, the Indian said that his people had learned of other white men like Anza, who now lived many days' travel to the west of them.

Anza's brows drew together thoughtfully. The Indian lived on the Gila River, north of Tubac. To the west of his home lay only unexplored territory. "How do you know that these are white men?" he asked.

The Indian became more excited. They had to be white men. They wore clothes like Anza's clothes. They carried muskets like Anza's soldiers. Moreover, they possessed a strange magic box in which was a small stick that moved.

Anza recognized the Indian's description of a compass. "How did you learn of these men?" His voice sharpened with interest.

The Pima had learned of the white men from the Yumas who lived many moons to the west. And the Yumas? They had learned from a tribe still farther west.

Anza could hardly conceal his excitement. The white men the Indian had described could only be Portolá and Father Serra in California! If the Indians were able to carry news all the way from the Pacific Ocean it meant that the desert beyond the Colorado wasn't impassable. There *was* a route from Sonora to the sea! If half-naked savages could cross this unknown land, then well-supplied Spaniards could do it too!

Giving instructions that the Pima was to be fed and rewarded, Anza returned to his quarters. It was hard to bring his mind back to routine reports. Time and again he pushed back his papers to stride impatiently back and forth across the small room. A dream was coming to life again, that long-ago dream of a twelve-year-old boy at Fronteras.

When Gálvez, the Inspector General, arrived, Anza told him what he had learned and offered to lead an immediate expedition overland to California. Gálvez seemed enthusiastic about the plan, but again Anza was doomed to disappointment. A new Seri uprising, followed by the serious illness of the Inspector General himself, delayed any action. Two long years dragged by.

By now a young Franciscan friar, Francisco Garcés, had replaced the Jesuit missionary at San Xavier del Bac, a lonely, isolated mission thirty miles north of Tubac. Father Garcés soon made it plain he was not one to remain at home waiting for converts to come to him. Riding alone, with only a little pinole, chocolate, and jerked beef for food, he made two trips to the villages of the Pima Indians along the Gila River. He so won their love that they affectionately dubbed him the "Old Man," in spite of the fact that he was not yet thirty years old. Like Anza, Father Garcés dreamed of finding an overland route, one which would link his small mission with those of his brother Franciscans in California. In 1772, when Anza learned that Father Garcés had returned from still another trip, this time down the Gila River as far as its junction with the Colorado, he hastily invited the young friar to Tubac.

On the morning of May 1 the sentry gave the alarm which meant that a lone rider was approaching from the north. Who but Father Garcés would dare to travel alone through this Indian-infested country? Anza hurried to the gate to greet his visitor.

Soldier and priest, they could not have been farther apart by calling. Even in physical appearance they were opposites. Anza was of medium height, muscular, and powerfully built, with a handsome, arrogant face and flashing black eyes. Father Garcés was tall and spare—a skinny scarecrow of a man—with a homely, bony face. Yet in the eyes of these two men burned the same lust for adventure.

Father Garcés already knew of Anza's proposal to discover an overland route to California. But now Anza could hardly wait to drag the friar away from the crowd which had gathered to the privacy of his own quarters. "Tell me, tell me quickly, did you really reach the Colorado?" he burst out impulsively as he sank into a cowhide-covered chair, motioning the friar to be seated.

Instead of accepting a chair, Father Garcés sank to the floor to sit cross-legged, Indian fashion, as had become his custom. His angular face remained impassive. From experience Anza had learned that it was impossible to drag words from the friar until he wished to speak. There were even a few unpleasant ones who claimed that, instead of teaching the Indians the way of the white man, Father Garcés had let them teach him the way of the Indians.

Anza could stand the silence no longer. "Tell me!" he burst out. "Did you really reach the Colorado?"

Anza's voice was so loud that even Father Garcés' meditation was shattered. As he lifted his head there was something like a twinkle in his usually somber eyes. "Yes, indeed, my good Captain. I not only reached the Colorado; I crossed it and went into the desert on the other side, along a range of mountains called the Cocopahs. Where they end in a great black peak I had to turn back. But from the peak I saw blue mountains beyond the desert and a pass near their summit."

"Blue mountains—the sierras of California!" Anza sprang from his chair. Unmindful of Father Garcés, still sitting cross-legged on the floor, he paced back and forth, very like a caged animal. "Mountains—that means water. Water—that means we can cross the desert. Father Kino was wrong: the desert cannot be as wide as he believed."

"It is true," Father Garcés nodded. "The desert is not as wide as we imagined. From the black peak you can see its end. But it still will be hard to cross it, much of the way without water."

"But it could be done?" Anza demanded, halting so abruptly that he almost fell over the friar.

Again Father Garcés nodded. "Yes, it could be done. Of course, we would have to plan our expedition carefully. Our best time to start would be in the winter. By starting then, we could cross the Colorado before the spring floods and reach the desert before the summer heat."

"We—*our?*" Anza's heavy eyebrows rose in astonishment.

"Of course, *our* expedition." Father Garcés rose. "My good Captain, surely you don't think I'll let you go off on an adventure such as this without taking me along!"

Anza, unaccustomed to having anyone tell him what to do, looked dumbfounded. Then his booming laughter filled the room. The hands of the two men met in a warm clasp of brotherhood.

There was much work to be done. Plans must be made, a petition sent to the Viceroy in Mexico City. Anza ordered food and wine. When the steaming platters of venison, chili peppers, and corn cakes were brought, Father Garcés sank again to his cross-legged position on the hard-packed earthen floor, attacking the food with both hands. Anza, already busy at his writing table, paid no attention to the peculiar eating habits of his friend, so great was his excitement.

It was after midnight before the first draft of the petition was completed. Since both were men of action rather than words, the request was simple and straightforward. Guided by the reports of the Indians as well as Father Garcés' discoveries, Anza asked permission to lead an expedition to find an overland route from Sonora to California, taking with him Father Garcés and twenty soldiers from Tubac, men he knew could be trusted for their ruggedness and devotion. Since successful accomplishment of the mission would bring sufficient riches and rewards, he offered to outfit the party at his own expense.

On May 2, 1772, the petition was completed and a courier dispatched to carry it the thousand miles to Mexico City It would be many months before a reply could be expected, so Father Garcés made ready to return to his mission. On the morning he left there was no need for long speeches. The two men clasped hands. Anza had found not only a friend, but a man with a dream to match his own.

The Captain watched until the tall, lank figure of the priest was swallowed by the desert. Then his eyes traveled to the distant spires of the Santa Rita mountains. Twenty-five years! Twenty-five long years had gone by since he had stood as a boy outside Fronteras. How much closer the mountains looked today!

Apaches Again

ANZA'S PETITION COULD NOT have reached Mexico City at a better time. Far from flourishing, the missions and presidios in California were barely maintaining a foothold. With their only source of supplies the uncertain arrival of the supply ships from San Blas, soldiers and friars were reduced to near-starvation. Even when the ships arrived, after the long voyage their foodstuffs were often rotting, livestock dead, and crews so weakened with scurvy they could barely unload their pitiful cargo. To the north there was an even grimmer threat. The Russians had landed in Alaska and there was a growing fear that they might move south before the Spanish could reinforce their hold on the new land.

Although Viceroy Antonio María Bucareli was one of the most foresighted administrators of New Spain, he was also a methodical man. First, a letter had to be dispatched to Carlos III in Spain. After that came endless consultations, and, finally, the presentation of Anza's petition to the junta, or war council, in Mexico City. The cautious junta withheld its decision.

In January, 1773, seven months after he had sent the petition, Anza received a reply. What a disappointment it was! Instead of the expected grant of permission, it was only a request for more information. Again Anza and Father Garcés met to draft more letters, Anza writing with terse words in a square, schoolboyish hand, Father Garcés with rambling, disjointed sentences in his painful, barely legible scrawl.

By now Father Serra himself was in Mexico City, having returned there on one of the supply ships to plead in person for assistance. He told a harrowing story of soldiers and friars with barely enough clothing to cover their bodies, reduced, at intervals between supply ships, to feeding on grasses of the fields. Though Father Serra had never met Anza, he was ready to support any proposal to find an overland trail to supply his missions.

In October, 1773, after a ride of a thousand miles in less than a month, a soldier, Juan Valdéz, arrived at Tubac with word for Anza and Father Garcés that their petition had been granted. The junta had accepted the original plan with only a few minor additions. Juan Valdéz was to accompany the expedition, since he had served in California and could act as a guide once the expedition crossed the mountains. Another friar was to be selected from one of the frontier missions as a companion for Father Garcés and to help keep records of the trip. (Tactfully, the reply did not mention that members of the junta had suffered enough from Father Garcés' miserable handwriting.) Lastly, on his return Anza was to report in person to Viceroy Bucareli in Mexico City.

This time the conference between Anza and Father Garcés was a joyous one. Since the date of departure was set for December 15, 1773, there was much work to be done. Selected to be Father Garcés' companion was Fray Juan Díaz, of the mission at Caborca, a sturdy young friar noted for his excellent penmanship. While Father Garcés returned to his mission to send messages ahead to his Pima friends along the Gila River to be expecting them, Anza began the task of gathering horses and supplies.

By the second of December, all was nearly ready. After one of Doña Ana's delicious home-cooked meals of turkey and venison, for the first time in weeks Anza fell into bed for a deep and satisfying sleep. Shortly before midnight the stillness was punctured by the sound of the sentry's musket.

"Juan! Juan!" Round-eyed, Doña Ana sat up in bed, her small plump hand reaching to shake her sleeping husband. The gesture was needless. With the first crack of the musket Anza was on his feet, as wide awake as though he had been doused with ice water. Even as Doña Ana struggled with the flint to light a candle, her husband had already jerked on his leather breeches. The door slammed behind him.

Outside in the darkened plaza, everything was wild turmoil. Soldiers in various stages of undress stumbled from the barracks, bumping into each other in the darkness. Then, above the excited voices came Anza's booming command, "Order, men! Order!" Miraculously, in what seemed only seconds, torches were lighted and the men were responding to discipline.

"The horses, Captain! The horses!" Corporal Sánchez managed a half-salute in spite of the fact that he was balancing a musket under one arm and trying to fasten his trousers with the other hand.

Seizing one of the torches, Anza was the first to burst through the presidio gates. In the moonlight, beyond the fort, the corral gates hung open. Only a few excited animals still milled about the corral, trying to find an exit. Rushing to close the gates before they too could escape, Anza barely glanced at the soldier guard lying face down, an arrow protruding from his back. Death by Indians was a common sight there on the frontier. One brief glance brought Anza the welcome knowledge that, since the man had not been scalped, the Indians were obviously in great haste and could not be far away. Then, far in the distance, came the muffled sound of galloping hoofs and a single, trailing Apache war whoop.

"To the saddle! Sánchez, Díaz, Ortega!" Anza barked. "To the saddle and after them!" Soldiers rushed to saddle and bridle the few remaining animals. Stopping only to force a bit between the teeth of a gray stallion, Anza leaped to the horse bareback and led the charge out of the corral.

Across the wheat field, past the winter-stripped skeletons of a fig orchard, the men galloped. "Turn them back before they reach the hills! Don't let them get into the mountains," Anza shouted.

A quarter league beyond the cultivated lands of the presidio, the men reined their horses to a stop. Around them the moonlit desert and blackened hills of the Santa Ritas lay lonely and quiet as a tomb. When someone brought a torch and Anza knelt to study the hoof prints in the sand, he knew there was no use in proceeding farther. It was a familiar Apache trick, melting into the hills as silently as they had come. Even that trailing war whoop could have been a decoy to lure the soldiers into pursuit while the main body of Apaches escaped with the horses.

Disheartened, the men turned back. By the time they reached Tubac, the soldiers who had stayed behind had finished their count. One hundred and thirty animals were missing, among them most of those intended for the expedition. In the morning Anza sent out search parties, but in his heart he knew that to do so was hopeless. By now, divided into small groups, the horses would be scattered through the hills, many of them already slaughtered since horse meat was considered prime eating by the Apaches. With heavy heart Anza sent a courier to inform Father Garcés of the loss.

Several days later Father Garcés himself arrived at the presidio, riding a gaunt and angular nag. One young soldier was heard to whisper that the mount was an excellent choice because she so closely resembled the good Father himself. But to Anza it was no time for jokes. He did not meet the friar at the gates. Instead, Father Garcés found the Captain in his quarters, busily writing letters.

The crushing news of the Apache theft had taken its toll on the friar also. Instead of squatting on the floor in his usual fashion, he sank gratefully into a cowhide chair. For once, Anza was thankful for that long interval of meditative silence. What was there to say?

"Your old enemies, the Apaches, eh?" Father Garcés said at last. "Well, there is nothing we can do but try to gather a fresh herd. With the good Lord's help we may still be able to make it across the desert before the end of winter. If not," he shrugged, "then we will be delayed another year."

"Delay! Delay! I tell you I will not be delayed again!" Anza began to pace up and down the narrow room. "We agreed the crossing was to be made this winter. Even if we are successful in getting new horses, how do we know the Apaches won't run them off too?"

Abruptly, he returned to the table where a large map lay open. "I too have been thinking. Our original plan was to head north to the Gila River, then follow it down to its junction with the Colorado. Without horses that is impossible now. But to the west, among our neighboring presidios and missions, we may be able to recruit new mounts." His finger moved across the map until it came to a stop at the presidio of Caborca one hundred and twenty-five miles to the west.

"I suggest that we change our route and go west first, gathering horses on our way down the Altar Valley. We will make Caborca our new starting point and from there head directly north to the Colorado itself."

Father Garcés frowned. "From Caborca to the Colorado is desert—"

"So it is desert!" Anza snapped. "Others have crossed it. If our men cannot cross one narrow strip of desert which others have crossed, what chance will they have when they reach the great unknown desert that lies beyond the river?"

A smile lit Father Garcés' solemn features. He unfolded his lanky frame from the chair. "You are right, Captain. We cannot delay longer. I like the plan. Not only will we be able to gather horses from the presidios, but by going down the Altar Valley my brothers at the missions of Saric, Tubutama, and Santa Teresa may help us also."

As though some great weight had been lifted from his soul and body, Father Garcés retreated to a corner where he sank more comfortably to the floor, spreading his brown robes about him. "And now, Captain Don Juan, though my spirit is restored I find that my frail human body is famished after the long ride. Perhaps it would not be too much to ask that we eat?"

With a laugh Anza sprang to the doorway. "Corporal Sánchez, food and drink for the good Father."

Two days later, Father Garcés returned to his mission to wait until the expedition was ready to start. Even with the new plan there would be a delay of several weeks while Anza secured enough horses to get the expedition under way.

When Anza received word that Bernardo de Urrea, the Commandante of the presidio of Altar, wished to see him, he felt sure that his request for horses had been granted. But it was not horses that awaited Anza at Altar.

"We too have had Apache raids," the Commandante told him. "We cannot spare you horses now, but we will try to have some waiting on your return. It was for quite another reason I sent for you," Urrea continued. "I have an Indian prisoner in my guardhouse. Frankly, I don't know what to do with the poor devil. He is a runaway from the Mission San Gabriel. Obviously he must be punished, but I thought I would turn him over to you."

"From Mission San Gabriel?" Anza's voice was incredulous. "You mean he has come safely across the desert all the way from California?"

"There is no doubt he has come from California," Urrea replied. "As to how safely, I will let you decide. When you hear his tale you may think again about this expedition of yours."

As soon as Anza had refreshed himself after the long trip from Tubac, the two men crossed the plaza to the guardhouse. Two soldiers brought forth the prisoner. As the trembling Indian was thrust forward, Anza saw that this was no ordinary savage. Though so tattered and threadbare that they barely covered his thin body, his clothes were the cotton shirt and pants of a white man. When addressed he replied in fairly fluent, though somewhat guttural, Spanish.

"Sebastián Tarabal," Urrea addressed the Indian. "This is Captain Anza of the presidio of Tubac. It is he who will decide your punishment."

The Indian flung himself to his knees, clasping his brown hands. "Good Captain, I meant no harm. I beg you, have mercy!"

"We will decide that later." Anza's voice was firm. "First, tell me your story."

With a look of relief, the Indian began his strange and pitiful tale. Born and raised at a mission in Baja California, Mexico, he had been taken by boat to the new California to help the Fathers in Christianizing and instructing the northern heathen at Mission San Gabriel. In time, finding the routine tedious, the Fathers overly strict, and overcome with homesickness, he decided to run away. Accompanied by his wife and a male relative, he had headed southeast, hoping to reach his tribe in Mexico. At first, the three had found the going easy through the lush valleys and over a pass in the mountains. It was only when they dropped down the far side of the sierra that they discovered the great desert. Tarabal's wife and relative perished in the burning waterless sands. Tarabal, more dead than alive, managed to crawl through the desert and was at last found by a party of wandering Yumas. At their camp on the Colorado, the Yumas nursed him back to health, then brought him to Sonora, hopeful of getting a reward.

Now Anza would decide his fate. When the Indian had finished his story, he fell once more to the ground. "Good Captain, whip me if you must. I beg only that you spare my miserable life."

Anza stepped forward to catch Tarabal's thin, wasted hand in his own strong one. He drew the Indian to his feet. "Do not fear. You have been punished enough already. From this day forward, Sebastián Tarabal, you will be my man. You will lead me to California."

Anza ordered one of his soldiers to gather together Tarabal's few pitiful possessions and to make ready a pack mule to carry the Indian back to Tubac. The Apache raid had not been all misfortune. Because of the delay the expedition had found a guide!

Ambush!

On Saturday, January 8, 1774, the expedition finally assembled in the courtyard at Tubac. In addition to Anza, Father Garcés, and Fray Juan Díaz, there were twenty soldiers from Tubac, the California soldier, Juan Valdéz, Sebastián Tarabal, a Pima interpreter, a carpenter, five muleteers, and two of Anza's personal servants. There were thirty-five mules loaded with provisions and sixty-five head of cattle which would supply food en route. When they had collected horses from the settlements to the west, the travelers hoped to have a herd of one hundred forty riding and pack animals.

All the four hundred inhabitants of Tubac gathered in the plaza for the farewell. Mass was sung. With all the ceremony and last-minute preparations and activity it was one o'clock in the afternoon before the bugle sounded and Anza gave the order to mount. Trailed by a band of children, barking dogs, and stragglers, the procession moved through the gates of the presidio. At the head of the company rode Anza, erect and proud in his oiled leather jacket and helmet. Next came the two brown-robed Fathers, then the soldiers, the pack animals and horses, and finally the cattle. For a small frontier presidio like Tubac, it was an impressive sight.

For a short distance the party traveled north in order to skirt a mountain range. Due to the late start, only three miles were covered that first day. Camp was made that night beside the ford of the San Xavier River. Early the following morning they set out once more, swinging westward now. This was Apache country but they were following a well-traveled route over which all had journeyed before. Even when the party was caught in a storm and was delayed for two days, the men laughed and joked around their campfires. With clearing weather, they dropped down from the mountains into the fertile Altar Valley. It was here that Anza expected to recruit horses.

This too was familiar territory. At every small settlement well-wishers hurried out to greet the expedition. Brown-frocked Franciscans embraced Fathers Garcés and Díaz, pressing upon them small gifts and last-minute prayers. The march took on the air of a festive parade.

Only Anza was grim-faced and solemn, taking no part in the merrymaking. His eyes were searching everywhere for the horses needed to carry his men safely over the long miles to be traveled. He made no effort to halt the gaiety of his men, however. As a seasoned campaigner, he knew the value of keeping up morale. Long months from now memories of this triumphal march would be cherished.

At the presidio of Altar Anza met his first disappointment. Here he was able to exchange a few tired mounts for fresh animals, but no extra horses were available. Two days later at Caborca it was the same story. Two strings of mules were brought before Anza. The animals were so scrawny and sharp-ribbed that he selected only two. Father Garcés and Díaz secured three more from the nearby missions.

Caborca was the last Spanish settlement to be passed through. Ahead lay a journey of more than two hundred and fifty miles across arid desert to the Yuma Crossing at the junction of the Gila and Colorado Rivers. Anza knew well that the success of the entire expedition could rest on the quality of their horseflesh. By now, however, time had become important. If the great desert beyond the Colorado was to be crossed while it was still winter, there must be no further delay. On the morning of January 22, just two weeks after leaving Tubac, without having secured the needed animals, Anza gave the orders to resume the journey.

The immediate objective was the tiny Pápago settlement of Sonóita, on the river of that same name, one hundred and twenty-five miles to the northwest. Anza had been as far as Sonóita on one of his previous campaigns. The Pápagos were supposed to have a truce with the Spaniards, but they had never taken to mission life. There was no way of knowing if they would be at peace now. However, it was not Indians who brought trouble to the travelers. The first night out of Caborca they were forced to make a dry camp. The second day they continued on through a desolate region dotted with desert plants—the great giant saguaro, choya, and palo verde. That night they found water for their animals by digging wells in the sandy bed of an arroyo. Ordinarily, the trip from Caborca to Sonóita could be made in three days. Now, with heavily laden pack animals and lumbering cattle, it required seven days and three dry camps.

At one time Sonóita had been the site of a mission, one of the chain founded by Father Kino. But after a Pápago and Pima uprising, in which the Father had been brutally tortured and killed, it had been abandoned. Anza found only crumbling ruins. Fortunately, however, the few Indian families living nearby proved to be friendly. The following day the expedition continued down the Sonóita River to a second camp near the present international boundary between Arizona and Mexico. Here would be the last running water until the Yuma Crossing was reached. Ahead lay a burning stretch of desert which, years later, would be dubbed the Devil's Highway. No longer would Anza's men be able to get water by digging wells in the sandy arroyos. From here on the only water they would find would be rain water left in potholes, or "tanks," in the rocks.

Anza was undaunted. He was armed with the maps Father Kino had made years before; also, Father Garcés had crossed this same desert only three years previously. In order to conserve what little water might be found, Anza ordered the party to divide. The main body, including horses and cattle, would start into the desert the following morning, leaving seven soldiers and the more heavily laden pack animals to follow one day later.

It was noon the next day before all the animals had been watered and the first division started into the desert. That night the travelers made dry camp. The following day they pressed on across a burning, dust-choked plain. To their right loomed a rocky range, for a distance the outcroppings appearing almost pure black, then almost white.

At mid-morning, when a muleteer reported that the men were having trouble making the slow-moving cattle keep up with the procession, Anza ordered a brief halt. He turned to confer with Father Garcés. "Well, good Father, is it good news or bad? Will we find water tonight?"

The friar, his face and robe so coated with dust he was barely recognizable, pointed toward the strange black-and-white mountain. "Good news, Captain. If my poor memory serves me, it is there in the mountains, just beyond where the black rock turns to white, that we will find the water."

Anza smiled. "That is what my maps say also. Water

at the black-and-white mountain, men!" He gave the signal to start on.

"Water—water at the pinto mountain—water!" In a great wave the word spread back through the party. It was almost as though the weary animals themselves understood and surged forward with renewed vigor.

But distances can be deceiving on the desert. It was well into the afternoon before the travelers finally reached their goal. Here, high on the mountainside in a narrow gorge, there would be water. Dismounting, Anza made his way up the precipitous slope, as much on his hands as on his feet. The water was there in a huge heart-shaped pothole in the rocks. But as he knelt beside the scum-encrusted pool his heart sank. There was not enough. . . . It was a moment of painful decision, decision that had to be his alone.

Slowly he rose to his feet and faced the expectant men below. In his enthusiasm, Corporal Sánchez was already halfway up the slope, leading his mare behind him. "If Sánchez quenches his great thirst, his faithful Pepita drinks too!" he boomed with a hearty laugh. At the sight of his commander's frozen face, he sobered. "What is it, Captain? Isn't there water?"

"Yes, there is water," Anza replied slowly. "But it is not for us. If we take this water there will be none left for our comrades who follow. Since we are traveling the lightest, it is we who must go without."

Such was Anza's power over his men that there was not a single grumble of protest. In groups of three or four, as swiftly as possible so that the thirsty animals below would not catch scent of the water and stampede, the men climbed to the tank. Each took several swallows of the faintly brackish water. Then, leaving eight soldiers behind to clear a trail to the tanks for the following party, Anza led the way on into the desert.

He knew that there was no chance of reaching the next water before nightfall but, to keep spirits up, the company traveled at forced march as though buoyed by great hopes. At nightfall the men stopped on the trail, overcome by weariness. Usually, they sang and joked around their campfires. That night there was no singing. One of the soldiers had brought along a violin. While weary men gazed into the coals, dreaming of loved ones, he played the Spanish melodies of home.

The following morning they pressed on through the desert hills. Shortly before noon, the company reached a watering place. As before, the tanks lay in a narrow side canyon. This time, however, there was no question of the water not being enough. Arranged one above another, like hollowed steppingstones, on the hillside were six kettle-shaped tanks connected by a common channel. At the sight of the water, cries of "Victoria" went up from the men. Cattle lowed and horses whinnied.

Dismounting, Father Garcés dropped to his knees in the sand. Taking off his leather helmet, Anza knelt beside him. A sudden hush fell upon the men. All those who were not occupied in controlling the animals knelt also. Together they offered prayers of thanksgiving. Anza named the potholes the Tanks of Purification in honor of the feast day, February 1, on which they had been reached.

After the animals had been watered, pasturage was found a short distance away. Since there was more than enough water for the entire party, Anza decided to wait here for the arrival of the others. When a messenger brought word that the pack train had reached the first tanks with its animals in such poor condition that they had to rest for a day, Anza sent back a relay of fresh animals. On the third day the entire party was reunited.

It was hard to say good-by to the life-giving waters of the Tanks of Purification, but on the fourth day the party started again toward the northwest. The following day, coming through a gap in the desert mountains, Anza drew his horse to a halt. Far in the distance across the desert was a long curving ribbon of green. Father Garcés pulled up beside him. "Yes, Captain," he said softly, "the cottonwoods of the Gila River."

That night camp was made beside a well in the shadows of the Gila Range. Just the sight of that distant greenery, the first trees seen since leaving Sonóita, had filled everyone with enthusiasm. Again there was merrymaking about the campfires. As was his custom, Anza strode from one fire to another, stopping to listen to a joke here, swap a story there, join in a song over yonder. It was only in those darkened intervals, walking between the fires, that his eyes were somber. The men could well celebrate, the Pápagos had proved harmless, and the first desert had been crossed safely.

But for Anza, upon whose shoulders rested the entire responsibility of the expedition, the solution of one problem meant only the beginning of another. In another day they would reach the junction of the Gila and Colorado. Would the Yumas be friendly? This could be the most important question of the entire expedition. For on the friendship of the Indians who controlled the Yuma Crossing depended not only the safety of his party but the future of any overland route to California.

"Your mouth smiles but your eyes worry," Father Garcés observed shrewdly as Anza sank down beside their campfire.

"Perhaps they would work more in concert if I knew what awaits us at the river," Anza replied somewhat gruffly.

"Chief Palma is a friend of the white man," Father Garcés replied. "He was friendly on my last visit."

"You came alone and unarmed, not with twenty soldiers, a herd of cattle and horses, and pack mules with supplies."

"I tell you there is no worry—" Before Father Garcés could continue he was interrupted by the sound of shouting from beyond the camp. Both men leaped to their feet. Seconds later, Corporal Sánchez and another soldier stepped into the firelight leading an Indian. "He claims he is a friend. He is a Christian, and his name is Luís," Corporal Sánchez explained. "He lives at Sonóita. He is returning from a trading trip to the Yumas and brings you a message."

Anza motioned to the shivering Indian to warm himself at the fire. "So you come from the Yumas?" Anza addressed him. "Do they know of our coming? They say Chief Palma is friendly to the white man."

The Indian nodded. "This is true. Chief Palma is friendly to the Spaniards. But the message does not concern Chief Palma. It concerns his brother Pablo who heads the tribes to the north. Pablo too has heard of your coming. He and his men want your horses and supplies. They plan to ambush you as you approach the river."

Anza's face was grim. "What of Chief Palma? Does he know of this plan?"

"Chief Palma has heard Pablo's boast. He has warned his people that they must not harm you. If they try, he says he himself will defend you," the Indian said.

"Can Palma control this Pablo?"

The Indian shook his head. "I do not think Pablo will listen to Palma. He has great greed. That is why my family and I decided to leave the river and come to warn you."

It was the first time the Indian had mentioned that his wife and children were traveling with him. Anza gave orders that all were to be fed and rewarded with beads and tobacco, and that a small fire of their own be set up for them nearby. When these arrangements had been made, Anza returned to stare moodily into the flames.

"I have seen this Pablo. He is a malcontent, a wild, ugly-looking creature," Father Garcés explained. "But

I do not think he carries much weight in the tribe."

"What if he should talk Chief Palma around to approve his plan?" Anza questioned.

"They are God's children, too. They will not harm us," Father Garcés replied, touching his cross.

Anza glanced sharply at the solemn face of the priest. He felt admiration for this simple man who had such a wonderful faith that he feared neither desert nor savage. But Anza was a soldier. His own faith was not so strong. To him, Luís's warning had answered his question. Tomorrow they would march in closed formation, ready for ambush!

Chief Palma

ANZA SLEPT LITTLE THAT night. At daybreak he sent an Indian on horseback to invite Chief Palma to ride out alone to meet him if his intentions were friendly. In view of the danger that might lie ahead, two Masses were sung and it was well into the afternoon before the last animal had been watered and the travelers resumed their march. At nine o'clock that night, having received no word from his messenger to Palma, Anza ordered a halt. But at dawn they mounted and continued on, the soldiers riding alert and in closed formation, across a shady plain dotted with green willows and cottonwoods.

At mid-morning a shout went up from the men as they saw a cloud of dust approaching from the northwest. Minutes later nine riders galloped into view. Anza saw that his scout was followed by eight Indians.

Unlike the Pimas, Pápagos and Seris, who were of short stature, the Yumas were tall and powerfully built. Many were over six feet tall. The braves were completely naked, their muscular bodies striped with grotesque markings of red-and-white clay. Sticks and feathers adorned their pierced ears. Several even wore feathers stuck through their noses, giving them a fierce warlike appearance. But Anza noted that only a few had bows and these were of extremely poor quality. Instead, it being midwinter, all carried firebrands which they moved continually up and down to warm their naked bodies.

One Yuma brave seemed to be a minor chief. He explained that it was with great regret that Chief Palma himself was unable to ride out to greet his visitors. He was away on a hunting trip. But, the brave went on to explain, he was to escort them to the river where the entire tribe was waiting to give them a friendly welcome.

As the party moved on toward the river, other Indians came to join it, some on horseback and some on foot. Soon there were women and children as well as men. The women, tall and robust like the men, also painted their bodies but all wore small skirts of woven grass and a few had capes of rabbit skins. By the time the travelers reached the Gila River, where they stopped to set up camp, they were surrounded by over two hundred babbling Indians of all ages. In spite of their ferocious appearance the Yumas were like children, crowding around the Spaniards, touching their clothing, poking fingers into the packs, and, from time to time, throwing great handfuls of dust into the air to show their delight.

At five o'clock, when a party of sixty braves rode into camp, a sudden hush fell over the people. At the head of the group rode a tall, stalwart brave with piercing black eyes and an arrogant face. Though he was naked and painted like the others, his haughty bearing, as well as the respectful silence of the other Indians, told Anza that finally he was facing the great Chief Palma.

The chief dismounted and came forward. With due ceremony Anza stepped to meet him, offering both hands in a sign of friendship. For a long minute the Indian chief and Spanish captain eyed each other. Then Palma ran forward. His muscular brown arms squeezed Anza in a crushing embrace. "Welcome! Welcome, white brother. My people have long awaited your coming."

Palma apologized for his absence when Anza arrived. Now he hoped to make up for the seeming slight. As for the Indians who had threatened to ambush the expedition, he had banished them from the area.

When Anza replied that he too came in friendship, Palma, overcome with emotion, hugged him again. Gathered in a huge circle, the Indians had been watching closely the greetings between their chief and the white captain. Now some began to shout, "The banner! The banner!"

Father Garcés stepped forward. It was plain that

many of the Indians remembered him from his visit three years before. The Father took a rolled silk cloth from his saddle pack. Anza had seen the banner many times. For Father Garcés it had become a kind of trademark, carried always on his visits to the savage tribes.

Unfurling the silken cloth, Father Garcés held it high so all could see. There were cries of delight and pleasure at the sight of the Virgin and Child. Standing proud and erect, Father Garcés turned the banner slowly so that all could see the beautiful figures. He waited until the shouting died away. Then abruptly, his face dark and threatening, he reversed the banner and showed the other side. This time there were shrieks of despair. Some of the Indians covered their eyes. On the other side, in the same glowing colors, was the picture of a lost soul in the burning torments of hell.

"This is the banner of my church," Father Garcés charged them in a ringing voice. "Which do you choose—the Mother of God or the torment of the infidel?"

Though there were few Indians who could understand his words, there was little doubt about the choice he offered. Again, in response to a clamor of requests, Father Garcés showed the Virgin and Child. Finally lowering the banner, he rolled it carefully and returned it to his pack. "You see, Captain," he said, turning to Anza with childlike simplicity, "they wish to become Christians."

Chief Palma nodded. "The brown-skirt speaks the truth, great Captain. My people desire that your God shall be their God." Palma had observed that the soldiers still remained alert, walking with scabbards open. "Tell your men to be at ease, Captain. My people will not harm them. They are like children. They only wish to examine your clothing and possessions. They will not steal."

Anza sensed that this was a crucial moment, to be handled with delicacy. Everything depended on the friendship of this Yuma chief. But did he dare to allow his men to lower their guard? Smiling warmly, he turned to the chief. "My men, too, wish to be friendly," he explained. "But they are warriors. As such, they must maintain discipline. You have been several times to the presidios in Sonora. Did you not observe that even there, though the soldiers were not fighting, they still walked about carrying their arms? It is part of their training."

Palma smiled. "I understand. I too have trained warriors."

Anza's face gave no sign of his obvious relief. A ticklish situation had been gracefully handled.

Aware that this was a solemn moment for the Indians, one which he could use to further their friendship, Anza motioned the entire tribe to gather about him. Summoning an interpreter, he explained that, in the name of his King, the mighty ruler of Spain and all the colonies, he was bestowing upon Palma the rank of the King's servant and ruler of the Yumas. He then hung a bronze medal, showing the head of Carlos III, on a red ribbon around Palma's neck.

The chief was so touched that tears filled his great dark eyes. "Master, master," he murmured.

Again, cries of joy went up from the Indians and the air was darkened with handfuls of dust which they threw about them. Anza chose this moment to drive home another point. He pronounced that there was only one God. He told his listeners that it was because God loved the Spaniards so well that He had given them so many fine possessions. If the Indians would show their love of God and the Spanish King, they too could expect rewards. But they must first give up their tribal wars and their practices of polygamy and nakedness.

When Anza had concluded, Palma talked to his people for more than an hour, interpreting the Captain's message. Finally, he asked them to go home for the night and leave the Spaniards to rest. So great was the Indians' curiosity that only a few obeyed. Most of them lingered around the camp all through the night, getting in the way and poking brown fingers into packs and supplies.

The next morning Palma himself led Anza down the Gila River to the best ford. Again the Indians accompanied them, shouting, dancing, and throwing dust. From infancy all Yumas had been trained to be excellent swimmers. Palma offered to have his braves carry the Spaniards' cargo across the river on their heads.

With no reason to distrust Palma, Anza ordered the animals unloaded. But, ever cautious, he forded the river first, with only half of the soldiers, so that the crossing would be covered from both sides.

First came the tallest and strongest Yumas, carrying the supplies on their heads; next the horses, and last the cattle and remaining soldiers. Father Garcés, who could not swim a stroke, was also carried across by the Yumas, stretched flat on his back, gazing skyward, hands folded quietly on his chest. By three in the afternoon the crossing had been completed.

Here, on an island formed by the junction of the Gila and Colorado Rivers, Anza found Palma's main encampment of nearly six hundred Indians. Hoping that his men might be left alone this second night, and wishing to repay the Indians, Anza ordered the distribution of gifts. In spite of Palma's promise that his people would not steal, Anza noticed some minor pilfering. The Yumas were particularly adept at using their feet for this. While a brave talked with a soldier, gesturing wildly with his arms, a limber brown toe would be neatly extracting some small object from one of the packs. In order that not a single person be overlooked, and that no one be rewarded twice, Anza ordered the entire tribe to form a single line. Childlike and eager, the Indians obeyed. Anza himself then went down the line, giving tobacco to each man, beads to each woman. It was dusk before the gift-giving was finished. Chief Palma thanked Anza on behalf of his people and again ordered them to disperse so that the Spaniards could sleep in peace. But it was the same story. Only a few obeyed. Indians hovered about the campsite throughout the night.

In the morning Anza faced the more treacherous crossing of the Colorado River on the other side of the island. Once more Chief Palma led the way to the ford. Though the timing had been perfect and the river at its most shallow, the crossing was still more than two hundred yards wide. Because of the depth of the water, this time the journey had to be made entirely by animal. But hundreds of Yumas, including women and small children, dived into the water and swam across in order to make certain that not one pack animal or lumbering cow veered from the safest course. Only Father Garcés again chose to make the crossing facing skyward, supported by the strongest braves.

By noon the ford had been completed successfully without the loss of a single animal. In honor of the occasion, the first crossing of the Colorado by the King's arms, Anza ordered a volley of musket fire, as well as the firing of small rockets. At the tremendous noise, the Indians fell to the ground, terror-stricken. Seconds later, realizing that no one had been harmed, they leaped to their feet with screams of delight and asked the Captain to make the big noise again.

Anza ordered the distribution of more gifts and the slaughter of several of the weakest cattle for a feast for all. That night in his tent he wrote a letter to Viceroy Bucareli telling of the successful crossing. A Yuma messenger would be chosen to carry it to the presidio at Caborca.

Camped that night on the west side of the Colorado,

Anza faced a new decision. To the west, still concealed behind the mountains, lay the great desert. The party could head north, following the Colorado River through unexplored country, hoping thus to circle the great desert on the north and to reach Monterey by the most direct route. Or it could proceed south down the Colorado and go westward across the desert, following the route previously taken by Father Garcés. Since Father Garcés had seen blue mountains beyond the desert, Anza decided on the southern crossing.

As the expedition followed the course of the Colorado through the thickets of cottonwoods, willows, and tules, the Yumas continued to accompany it. Chief Palma himself rode proudly by Anza's side, the new medal bouncing grandly on his brown chest. Hundreds of naked savages raced beside them, stumbling over themselves in their eagerness to help clear the brush and drive the animals. Even the more timid women and children trailed behind, devoting their attention to the cattle, four or five driving each bewildered animal.

As the procession passed smaller encampments along the river, Anza ordered brief halts so that more gifts could be distributed. At the end of the second day they reached a village which was somewhat larger than the former ones. Several braves, accompanied by their swarthy, heavy-set leader, rode out to meet the travelers. Palma introduced the chief as his brother Pablo. Anza studied the Indian closely. So this was Pablo, the malcontent?

It was obvious that Pablo resented Palma's presence. Ignoring his brother, he gouged bare heels into the sides of his horse, whirling it in frantic circles for the Spaniards' benefit. "Not just Pablo!" he shouted, beating his chest. "Captain Pablo . . . mightiest captain of the river!"

"Captain Pablo indeed!" Anza heard one of his soldiers grunt in Spanish. "Captain Feo, I'd say!"

The name, Captain Ugly, was well applied. Unlike Palma, who was extremely handsome, Pablo was of shorter stature, of tremendous muscular build, with much blacker skin, and a flattened nose so pierced with huge feathers and sticks that his face resembled a porcupine. "Captain Pablo, the greatest, the bravest . . ."

In deference to Palma, Anza gave no heed to Pablo's boastings. When gifts were distributed he was given only the small additional amount allotted to a lesser chief. It was apparent Pablo was annoyed by the slight. Without thanking the Captain, he wheeled about rudely and left the camp, shouting noisily as he went.

That night, as the Spaniards settled about their campfire, Anza was aware of Pablo and his men a short distance away. The Indian chief glowered in the direction of the Spaniards' camp and continued his wild singsong comments. Worried, Anza summoned an interpreter. "What is Pablo saying?" he inquired.

The Indian, embarrassed, looked away. "It is not important," he said.

"Tell me. It *is* of importance!" Anza insisted.

The Indian shrugged. "Pablo makes boasts. He tells

his men you are small in number; they could easily kill you and steal your possessions."

Anza stared grimly into the glowing coals. Palma had already told him that in another day he and his Indians would have to turn back. Would Pablo dare to follow the Spaniards into the desert and there attempt the ambush? Abruptly Anza made his decision. Summoning his soldiers, he ordered them in closed ranks with scabbards bared. At their head he strode toward Pablo's campfire.

At the approach of the Spaniards Pablo and his braves rose to their feet. "Captain Anza wishes to speak with Chief Pablo," Anza announced in a booming voice.

"What does Captain Anza want? Does he not know Captain Pablo is the bravest, the great—"

Rudely Anza interrupted. "Captain Anza has heard that Pablo desires war with the Spaniards. All right! If that is what you want you shall have it now. Step from behind your fire and my men shall meet your braves on this spot."

Pablo looked startled. His brows drew together and he threw Anza a venomous look. Already several of his braves were fitting arrows to their bows. Glowering and muttering under his breath, Pablo strode dramatically back and forth beside the fire. Abruptly he turned. Anger was gone; his eyes were beseeching. "The great Captain hears wrong. Pablo is only a poor chief. Pablo loves the Spaniards. Pablo is a friend," he whimpered pitifully.

A moment later he stepped around the fire as if to embrace the Captain. Anza stepped back haughtily, avoiding the chief's arms. "See that you prove your friendship then!" he said coldly. Turning his back, he returned to his own fire.

The bluff had worked. Somehow Anza sensed that there would be no further danger from Chief Pablo. As he sat down again beside the fire, Palma, who had been watching with his own braves in readiness, sank beside him. "The Captain must forgive my brother," he apologized. "He is a braggart and a fool!"

A brief smile flickered across Anza's face. If it had not been that his men were so hopelessly outnumbered, he might have laughed. He had not dealt with the Indians for twenty-five years without learning something about handling them. "You may tell your brother I will consider forgiving him," he announced with great condescension.

Anza then ordered a soldier to slaughter one of the poorest beeves and distribute a bit of the meat to Pablo and his followers as well as to the other Indians.

The following day many of the Yumas started turning back. Swinging inland from the river, Anza and his men camped beside a lake formed by overflow in the flood season. It was a green and fertile spot and they named it Santa Olaya. Here Chief Palma told Anza that he would be unable to accompany him any farther since they had now entered the territory of the Cojats and Cajuenches, his tribal enemies. It was a sad moment of parting. Since they had met beside the Gila, Palma had never left Anza's side, so great was his adoration of the Spanish Captain. Now the haughty chief burst into tears. He promised that he and his people would await the Spaniards' return. If the river was at flood stage, Anza was not to worry; the Yumas would build rafts to ferry the men across.

The chief's devotion was so plainly sincere that even Anza's eyes misted. After his years of Indian fighting he had never dreamed of feeling such affection for a savage. Dismounting, he and Palma embraced warmly. *"Hermanos todos*—brothers all." The two words were enough to seal a lifetime bond.

Defeat At The Dunes

"VAYAN SUBIENDO!" ANZA'S RINGING voice gave the order to mount.

If the men's faces were grim as they swung into their saddles it was with reason. Ahead lay the great desert, the most dangerous part of the journey. Even the date, the thirteenth, seemed one of ill omen. But Anza was a soldier, not an old woman who plotted her life by signs and portents. He moved when men and animals were ready. Moreover, in addition to Tarabal and Father Garcés, he now had four Cojats and one Yuma Indian to act as guides.

Accompanied by a great cloud of dust, the expedition pulled away from the blue waters of Santa Olaya. After traveling a short distance the men dropped into the dry wash of the Paredones River which, the guides explained, was the usual route taken by the Indians.

Perhaps the river bottom was a fair trail for a handful of savages but not for a caravan of this size. The soft sand sucked at the animals' hoofs until they were slowed to half their normal pace. Men coughed and choked in the rising blanket of dust. In disgust Anza motioned everyone out of the wash. To his dismay, he found the arid plain, with its sharp rocks and spiny cactus thickets, even worse. Finally, with a grudging look at the guides, he ordered a return to the slow progress of the river bed.

The purple shadows of evening were painting the gullies before a scout rode back to report water and pasturage ahead.

The men found water for themselves by digging in the sandy arroyo; but there was none for the stock and the sparse, alkali-tinged grass would not begin to go around. When the grass was gone the animals nosed out less attractive herbs growing among the cactus.

The men had barely started breaking camp the next morning when Corporal Sánchez stepped across the blackened remain's of Anza's campfire. He saluted. "Captain, the guides wish to speak to you."

Anza glanced toward Father Garcés with lifted eyebrows. Perhaps today they were going to be able to leave the slow progress of the wash for a faster trail. Minutes later, as the Indians were brought before him, his hopes vanished. Hanging their heads and shifting their brown feet nervously, all five refused to meet his eye. The interpreter explained. "They are sorry. They cannot go farther with you. They have shown you the trail and now they must turn back."

"Turn back!" Anza shouted. "They promised to lead us across the desert. All they have done is to bog us down in this miserable river bottom. We haven't even made a real start!"

There was a mumbled exchange of words. The Indians shook their heads. "They cannot go on. You are entering the land of their enemies," the interpreter explained.

"They have seen my soldiers' arms. Tell them that we will protect them," Anza replied.

The guides were stubborn. "Misfortunes come to those who cross into the lands of their enemies," the interpreter elucidated.

Anza was too wise to plead further since he knew that the guides could desert easily enough whenever they wished. He shrugged as though the matter were unimportant. "Tell those who have broken their word that I shall now break mine. They will not receive the fine reward I had planned for them. But those who are loyal and stay with me shall receive double." Two of the Cojats exchanged glances. Greedier than their brothers, they agreed to continue. But nothing could keep the other three from melting into the desert.

The hot morning sun had burned the soldiers' faces even before they were ready to march. To the west they could make out the hazy outline of the barren Cocopah Mountain. To the north an arid, desolate wasteland stretched to the horizon. As the weakened animals stumbled and struggled through the clutching sands all hopes of making more speed that day disappeared like the hot air rising from the wash.

Spirits lifted when, after only a few miles, the guides announced that water was ahead. Though scum-encrusted and far from appetizing, the pools were larger than those from which the men had drunk the night before. They named the spot Halfway Wells.

While the thirsty men were drinking the two Cojat guides asked to speak with Anza again. Far to the north, barely visible through the blue haze that hugged the desert, a solitary peak stood above the horizon. One of the Indians explained that it was at this distant peak the expedition would find a good water supply. He and his companion could go no farther.

"What about your promise? What about your fine reward?" Anza wheedled, knowing that he could no longer afford to be imperious.

The Indians shook their heads. "The people who live beyond this arroyo are very bad," they said.

Anza glanced across the sun-bleached plain. It was hard to imagine any people, good or bad, living in such a waterless waste. He offered to triple the rewards.

Even greed had lost its power. The two Indians glanced uneasily toward the desert. "Bad people, very bad people," they repeated.

"It is no use, Captain. You cannot force them to go on. They will only run away at the first chance," Father Garcés broke in. "Though we are farther north than the route I followed three years ago, I have recognized landmarks and we still have the Indian, Tarabal."

Anza knew the friar was right. The Indians had pointed out Signal Mountain, near the present-day boundary of Mexico and California, where the next water would be found. Beyond Signal Mountain lay more desert, then the sierras of California. Though hidden now by the midday haze, the far blue line of the mountains had been visible earlier in the clear morning air. From now on the expedition would have to carve its own route.

While the soldiers were resting, the slower moving pack animals caught up with them. One look at the stumbling animals told Anza that they could go no farther that day. Tomorrow men and animals would need all their strength to cross safely the miles of desert that lay between them and that distant peak.

"Vayan Subiendo!" Anza's command rang out at dawn the following morning. Being toughened soldiers, a few hours' rest was all the men needed to restore their vitality. Unfortunately, the animals had not fared as well. Bad water and scanty feed had weakened all of them. Desperate in their hunger, some had eaten semi-poisonous herbs that caused them to slobber continually. But there was no cure for them here at the brackish water of Halfway Wells. Their only hope, along with that of their masters, lay in reaching fresh water and pasturage at Signal Mountain before nightfall.

Yet spirits were high as men took their places. In the crisp morning air Signal Mountain appeared much closer than it had the night before. Then, less than two miles from camp, a scout, traveling ahead, let out the welcome cry, "Water!"

"Water! Water ahead!" Croaking voices sent the word back through the procession until even the dust-masked faces of the muleteers broke into grins. Anza spurred his horse forward to the blue-green pool. Kneeling, he scooped up the water in his cupped hands. Choking, he spat it out again. "Alkali!"

It was bad enough having to tell his thirsty men that they could not drink, but now at the rear of the procession the parched cattle and pack animals had scented the water. They surged forward, lowing and braying, unaware that the pool could mean death. Any disappointment the men might have felt was lost in their frantic efforts to stop a stampede. There were sighs of relief when finally all of the animals had been driven into the desert, safely away from the bad water.

A short time later, the party crossed a sand dune that blocked the arroyo and the cry of water sounded again. It brought little response from the men. But when some of them who rode ahead dug into the moist sand, they found sweet water, better than any they had encountered since leaving Santa Olaya. By deepening the hole in the sand to several feet, they made the water flow a little faster. Someone dubbed it the Deep Well of Little Water.

Refreshed, they marched into the desert again. As the sun rose higher Signal Mountain seemed to retreat into the surrounding haze rather than to draw closer. Soon more dunes blocked the way. At first an attempt was made to go around them. Later, in places where one dune seemed to join another, there was nothing to do but to go over them, animals thrashing and slipping as shifting sands grabbed at their straining legs. The faintly sucking sands of the Paredones River seemed like a paved highway now in contrast to these hungry sand dunes.

Summoned to Anza's side, Tarabal proved of little help. It was somewhere here in this wasteland that his wife and relative had died and he himself had suffered from delirium so that he could neither remember his route nor the place where the Yumas had found and saved him.

They now seemed to be on a great plain covered entirely with dunes. At times the distant peak, the travelers' goal, was lost behind mounting hills of sand. Efforts to go around one dune only brought one face to face with another. To add to the misery of the men the wind had come up now, moving the surface sand so that, glancing ahead, they seemed to be wading into a great shimmering, swirling sea. Some men rode with pieces of cloth across their faces, others with an arm crooked to shield their eyes. At the crest of one dune Anza turned to look back at the struggling procession behind him. With the passing of such a herd of animals, a blazed trail of hoofprints should extend behind them to the horizon. Not here among the dunes. Moving sands filled in tracks as soon as they were made, erasing the route of progress as cleanly as though the expedition were being swallowed forever.

Father Garcés reined up beside Anza. "A man who leaves no footprints seems as unearthly as the man who casts no shadow," the Father said, as though reading the Captain's thoughts.

"I am not so much worried about what I leave as what I face," Anza replied dryly. He motioned toward Signal Mountain, which seemed as far away as ever, and the dunes that appeared to stretch all of the way to its base. "There is no need to alarm the men, but we cannot reach the mountain by nightfall. A few more leagues of this sand and most of the animals will not reach it at all. I have been thinking. We must divide the party. The weakest men and animals must turn back now while they still have the strength to get back to the Deep Well of Little Water. From there they can return to the Colorado and Chief Palma's village to wait for me. With a small party of only the strongest men and horses I will go on to California."

"No," Father Garcés protested. "The Cojats warned of hostile peoples ahead. Divided, we would be at the mercy of both the savages and the desert. We are a small enough band now. We must all turn back or all make it together."

Anza was unconvinced. "The muleteers say that the pack animals cannot go farther. Would you have us stick together just so the strong can perish with the weak?"

"We must trust in God."

"There are times when I prefer to trust my own two strong legs and those of my horse!" Anza replied with a sudden flash of temper. For a moment the two strong-willed men glared at each other. Then anger vanished as quickly as it had come. Anza not only respected Father Garcés as his spiritual advisor but as an experienced explorer as well.

Within minutes they were plotting a compromise. Half of the supplies would be sent back to the Deep Well of Little Water with a small guard of soldiers. The soldiers would be sent for once the others reached Signal Mountain. After bidding good-by to the men who were turning back, the others plodded on into the dunes. Even with their lightened loads, the pack animals soon dropped behind. They began to slip and fall. Soon the soldiers were walking to spare their exhausted mounts. When they reached a small rise and still saw no end to the dunes, Anza knew that they could go no farther. He realized now just how much that Apache raid on their horses had cost them. His valiant men had the spirit to go on but lacked the animals to carry them.

In his role as a commander Anza had grown accustomed to hiding his true emotions from his men. But as he signaled for a halt his heart filled with a terrible despair.

Father Garcés, his brown robes dripping sand, rode up beside him. Far from looking dismayed, his usually solemn face shone with excitement. Turning in the saddle, he pointed toward the southwest to where a knobby black mountain of volcanic rock protruded from the desert floor. "See that mountain? I recognize it from my trip three years ago. There is an Indian village at its base and plentiful water."

"Are you certain, Father?" Anza questioned. "It lies to the south and out of our way."

"I am certain," Father Garcés insisted.

Anza knew that it could spell doom for the expedition if the friar were wrong, but there seemed even less hope in trying to go forward. He sent a message to the trailing pack train and cattle herd, ordering them to turn directly toward the black mountain. Then he and his soldiers headed south also. Gradually the dunes dropped behind them and the way became easier. Still, it was close to dusk when they reached the base of the black mountain. They found neither Indian village nor any water.

"I know this is the mountain. It *has* to be the mountain!" Father Garcés cried in a stricken voice.

"Many mountains look the same on the desert," Anza tried to comfort him.

"I am to blame. I am the one who has led you astray!" The friar's face had turned gray with consternation.

Anza spurred his mount closer to that of his friend. His hand reached for the friar's. "We must put our trust in the Lord." He was repeating the advice that Father Garcés had given him only hours earlier in his own time of crisis. There was no need for more words. Their hands clung for just one moment in that warm clasp of friendship.

Even when the weary men had bedded down on the

desert floor, Father Garcés insisted on continuing his search for the lost village on into the night. Anza sent two soldiers with him for protection. It was dawn when they returned, having found nothing. "There seems little hope. What shall we do now?" the Father asked.

"We must return as quickly as possible to the Deep Well of Little Water," Anza replied. "Some of the animals died during the night. We must get back to water before the others perish too." Already he had given word to Corporal Sánchez to awaken the men.

It was not the clinging sands that slowed them now but exhaustion instead. Only a short distance from the black mountain they spotted the dust of the pack train and the cattle coming to meet them. Anza sent a messenger with the news that there was no water and that they must turn back. It was two o'clock that afternoon before the first soldiers staggered into the tiny oasis at the Deep Well of Little Water, most of them walking now and leading their animals. It was nightfall when the stock arrived, a number of the animals having died along the way.

Here at the desert well, with its scant supply of feed, there was no hope of the sick and dying animals regaining their strength. And so began the slow and heartbreaking retreat to the Colorado River.

Camped once again at Halfway Wells, Anza addressed his men. He praised them for their strength and courage during the recent ordeal, reassuring them that they were still going on to California. He told them of his new plan. The heavily laden pack train was their biggest handicap and so he had decided that half of their supplies would be left at Chief Palma's village, along with a soldier guard. Once the pack animals had recovered, the main party, traveling light and using the strongest of them, would make another attempt at crossing the desert.

This time even Father Garcés had to agree with the plan.

"On to California!" someone shouted.

"We're with you, Captain!" another voice rang out.

"The devil take the horses. If they die in the sand dunes, we'll follow you on foot to the new land!" still another cried. As with one voice, men who could barely croak through parched lips only hours before were shouting and shrieking their determination to follow Anza to the ends of the earth if necessary. Anza turned away quickly, unaccustomed moisture in his eyes. What was one small defeat in the face of such loyalty!

On To San Gabriel

TEN DAYS AFTER THAT ill-fated Friday the thirteenth when they had started so hopefully into the desert, Anza and his men stumbled back to the green pastures and blue lagoon of Santa Olaya.

With two exceptions, the next few days were ones of rest for both weary men and animals. Barely taking time to see to the comfort of his men, Anza sent an urgent summons to Chief Palma at his village farther up the river, then began planning the strategy for his next attack upon the desert. Father Garcés, undaunted by the recent desert ordeal, asked permission to take off on some private explorations of his own.

Anza, who had been counting on the friar's assistance, frowned. "I would have thought you had seen enough unknown territory for awhile."

"This will not be unknown country. I plan only to

go downstream and renew old friendships at some of the villages I visited three years ago. Who knows, I might uncover some information that will help us."

A man of action himself, Anza understood his friend's restlessness but there was a twinkle in his eye as he answered him. "It couldn't be that you also hope to uncover the mystery of what happened to that disappearing village?"

For a moment Father Garcés' bony face looked as guilty as a schoolboy's. "All right, Captain, I admit that was in my mind too. The wondrous mysteries of God I accept. But mysteries created by poor earthbound mortals like myself need an explanation."

Anza laughed. Though no one held it against the Father for having led the party astray, it was plain that the priest would never rest until he had discovered the reason for his error. Anza wished him well. "Only see that you are back by March first or I shall go on to California without you," he warned gruffly.

A few hours later, armed with only a small pouch of food, some beads and tobacco, and his unwavering faith, Father Garcés rode out of camp alone. Anza did not worry about his safety. The adventurous friar was quite capable of taking care of himself.

He waited impatiently for the arrival of Chief Palma. When the chieftain finally rode into camp, still proudly wearing the medal Anza had given him, he embraced Anza warmly and wept for the Captain's misfortune.

As before, Anza's heart warmed at the seeming sincerity of the Yuma chief, but his long years as an Indian fighter made him wary. A born leader, he found it hard to be dependent on anyone, let alone a naked savage. Yet he knew that the safety of his party, as well as the future of any overland trail between Mexico and California, was going to depend on the loyalty of this arrogant and childlike Indian chief. It was difficult to trust this man, even though he realized he must.

Anza tossed sleeplessly that night, considering the problem. Was it because of his own pride and arrogance that he could not put his faith in another person? Was it because of his long experience with Indian treachery that he could not fully accept Palma's offer of friendship? Seldom in his life had he been drawn to any man as he was to this tall, handsome Indian. Yet from childhood he had been taught that Indians were enemies, and he had been schooled to obey his mind, not his heart. He wished that Father Garcés were there to advise him. Yet something told him that perhaps it was best that the priest was absent. The decision must be his alone. By morning Anza had made up his mind.

Summoning Palma, Anza told him of the great trust he was going to place in him. Most of the expedition's supplies and pack animals and all of its cattle would be left with the Yumas while Anza and his men, traveling with only the barest provisions, would go on to California. It would be up to Palma to guard the travelers' belongings until their return.

Before he had finished speaking, something told

Anza that he had made the wise decision. Palma's brown face glowed with pride. "Never fear, my brother. We will take such good care of your animals that we will not let one of them die. If anyone dares touch your supplies, I myself will kill the thief." He made a plunging motion toward his brown chest.

Anza had not expected quite such ardor but he thanked Palma for his devotion.

On hearing of Anza's return, the curious Indians once again flocked by the hundreds around the white men's camp. In Father Garcés' absence, young Father Díaz gave them simple religious instruction. Teaching them to say "Ave Maria" was not difficult, but when they brought him their pagan idols to be smashed, even Anza agreed that he had made unexpected progress.

This time the Indians were not so shy. They particularly liked the music made by the soldier with the violin. Some of the soldiers taught the younger Indian women to dance the fandango. In the evening, seated side by side in the firelight, Anza and Palma watched the twirling dancers while Palma talked of the day when the Spaniards would send missionaries and settlers to live among his people. It would have been easy for Anza to linger, enjoying this lazy life, but, even as he listened politely to the chief, his mind was filled with other plans.

He was relieved, on March 1, when a sentry's cry rang out and Father Garcés, dusty and travel-worn, rode into camp. The following day, with twenty-four men and ten pack animals carrying supplies for one month, Anza rode out of Santa Olaya to make a new assault on the desert. Behind him he left three muleteers and several other men to assist Palma with the stock and supplies.

Anza's new plan was to go around the dunes by heading directly west, then to follow the Cocopah Range to a jumping-off place across the desert at Signal Mountain. Father Garcés would have preferred a northern route, mainly for its chance to see new country, but he agreed to the route Anza had chosen.

As the travelers left Santa Olaya, crowds of Yumas swarmed about them. But gradually the Indians dropped behind, all except two braves who planned to accompany Anza all the way to California.

For the first few days the men were still traveling through country fed by the overflow of the Colorado and water was no problem. They passed through several Indian villages and found the natives friendly. At the second village Father Garcés finally discovered the answer to the mystery of his mountain. When some of the Indians ran out crying, "Jesus," "Maria," Father Garcés recognized them as the Indians whom he had instructed three years ago in the village at the black mountain. From them he learned that the village's water supply had dried up and the people had been forced to move. On the desert it had not taken long for shifting sands to cover the site where their homes had once stood. Anza was glad that Father Garcés had found his answer. The priest seemed to sit a little straighter in the saddle after that.

The following day brought the beginning of the march into the desert and a warning from the Indians that there were many miles to cross to the next water supply. To make the going easier, Anza ordered a divided march. That night the men made their first dry camp. The sun had barely risen the next morning before they were on their way again, knowing that a good forty miles of desert lay between them and water. They could see Signal Mountain beckoning ahead now, but they had not encountered any sand dunes. In high spirits, the soldiers renamed the peak Impossible Mountain because of the way it seemed constantly to recede instead of drawing closer as they marched.

That night, after going through a rocky pass in the Cocopah Mountains, they found some marshy springs near a large salt lake. When the men found the remains of some ocean fish around the edge of the lake, they realized that the lake must be formed by a seasonal overflow from the Gulf of Mexico. The discovery proved a bad sign. Before half of the animals had been watered, the fresh water spring turned to salt. But the soldiers refused to be dismayed. Even if their Impossible Mountain had a way of eluding them, the long blue sierras beyond the desert were growing closer and their Indian guide had promised that tomorrow they would find fresh water ahead in a side canyon.

In the morning Anza learned that the guide had vanished during the night, in such haste that he had left all his belongings. Remembering the disaster that had followed the desertion of their guides on the first trip, Anza sent Corporal Sánchez and a scouting party ahead to search for water. They found it in a rocky canyon, just as the Indian had promised. The following day Corporal Sánchez rode ahead again. This time he captured six wandering Indians and from them learned the way to the next water. The springs were located in a bleak and desolate spot on the desert, the ground almost bare of vegetation, though covered with hundreds of flat black rocks. Yet among the men there was great rejoicing, for their Impossible Mountain loomed beside them now. These were the same springs they had been trying to reach when they had been turned back by the dunes!

Soon there was cause for even more joy. While the laughing, joking men crowded around the springs, watering their animals, Tarabal wandered away from the group to stare across the desert. Suddenly he gave a great cry. He rushed to Anza.

"Captain, my Captain! I remember this place. I know the trail now—all the way to the Mission San Gabriel!" At his words a tremendous cheer went up from the men.

There was still desert to cross, but Tarabal assured them that two days' journey without water would bring them safely to springs on the far side. Anza ordered a thirty-hour rest to prepare both men and animals for this final test of strength before they started into the desert again. The ordeal was not yet over. The men camped the first night without water and the next morning had barely started on their way when they found the route once again blocked by sand dunes. But this time they did not flounder into them helplessly. True to their oath at Halfway Wells, the soldiers dismounted. Leading their mounts, they headed into the dunes on foot. The sand pulled at their ankles. In some places it rose to the calves of their legs. They soon found that men as well as animals could stumble and fall. At first a few of the younger men tried singing. When this became impossible because of the swirling, choking clouds of dust, they lowered their heads and plodded on doggedly.

Before nightfall they had come through the dunes and reached the springs that Tarabal had described. They promptly named the spot San Sebastián in honor of the saint. The unknown desert had been crossed. Towering above them now were the blue sierras of California.

The arrival of the Spaniards at the spring surprised a party of Indians who were camping there. Terrified, they fled, leaving all their possessions. Anza sent Tarabal to bring the Indians back. He returned with a single woman, so frightened that she had to be dragged into camp. Anza gave her tobacco and beads and told her to fetch the rest of her people so that they too could be given presents. She scampered away like a wild animal, to return a short time later leading seven braves. These were Serranos, the Mountain People of California. Less advanced than the Yumas, they did not cultivate crops, but lived on small game and wild herbs and were terror-stricken at their first sight of horses. However, to Anza's surprise, they could understand the language of the two Yumas who were in his party and he suggested that the two tribes become friends.

The following morning minor disaster befell the travelers when they lost several animals in a salt bog beyond San Sebastián. But from there on Tarabal knew the route. The next day they learned from another party of Indians of the ocean three days to the west and of other white men only six days away. They climbed steadily from desert foothills to the forested slopes of the mountains and, on March 15, 1774, crossed the mountains at the Pass of San Carlos.

On the other side of the Pass they dropped swiftly down into lush meadows filled with wild flowers; they discovered canyons where oaks and cottonwoods grew. Though the men no longer lacked feed for their half-starved animals, many beasts were in such poor condition that their riders proceeded on foot. There was little grumbling, however. The way was easy now, with the end of the long journey almost in sight.

Only one obstacle remained. The Santa Ana River was at flood stage because of melting snows and spring rains. Traveling along the river bank, Anza finally located a huge log jam. He ordered his men to fell some trees, adding them to it until a bridge had been formed across which the animals could be led. Two days later, they forded the more shallow San Gabriel River and saw ahead the rough adobe and log buildings of the mission.

Brown-robed friars and soldiers, wearing the tattered blue-and-red uniforms of the King of Spain, poured from the buildings to greet them. The mission bells began to ring and there was a volley of musket fire. "Victoria!" "Victoria!" "Victoria!" The cry came from all directions.

Friars embraced their brothers, Father Díaz and Father Garcés. Soldiers slapped each other on the back. With tears in his eyes, Father Paterna, Superior of the mission, seized Anza's arm. "Sonora! Is it really true? Is it really true that you and these men have ridden on horseback all the way from Sonora?" he repeated over and over again, as though he could not believe this miracle.

"Yes, indeed, Father," Anza assured him. "We have come all the way by land and not lost one man's life along the trail."

An overland route between Mexico and California had been opened at last!

The Hard-Riding Captain

THE DAY AFTER THE expedition's arrival at San Gabriel Mission was one of celebration. Father Paterna led the Thanksgiving Mass. Anza's soldiers broke open their remaining food packs and there was a hearty meal for everyone. Knowing that his soldiers deserved at least one day of relaxation without worry or strain, Anza said nothing, but already his eyes told him that things were not well at the mission. The robes of the friars were no more than threadbare rags. While the mission Fathers had eagerly prepared the meal for the hungry explorers, they had contributed only a little corn meal.

The next morning Anza met with Father Paterna in his quarters and learned the sad truth. The supply ship from San Blas was long overdue. The supplies at the mission were so low that the Father Superior and his men were living on three tortillas a day, plus what herbs each man could find for himself in the fields. "But the little we have we shall gladly share," Father Paterna insisted.

Anza thought regretfully of the supplies and cattle left on the Colorado, but it was too late to do anything about them now. "We cannot accept such an offer," he replied. "The welcome guest soon becomes unwelcome when there is no food in the cupboard. Our real goal is the capital at Monterey and we must move on immediately."

Even as these words left his lips, Anza realized how impossible this was going to be. He had been counting on getting supplies at the mission. Without them, his men would not have enough food to reach Monterey. Had they come safely across the terrible desert only to starve in California?

Father Paterna was an observant man too. "The Lord has always helped us before. We must ask Him to provide for us again," he said.

The priest had barely finished speaking when a commotion arose outside. Anza was first to reach the door with Father Paterna, brown robes flapping, close behind. In the courtyard soldiers and friars were gathered around a man on horseback. "The New Galicia and Father Serra have reached San Diego! The supply ship has arrived!" the man shouted.

Anza and Father Paterna exchanged wondering looks. Certainly God had answered their prayer with swiftness.

Anza sent several soldiers and fifteen pack animals

to San Diego to pick up the needed supplies for the mission. Two days later, restless with waiting, Father Garcés set out after the soldiers on the flimsy pretext of finding some instrument that could be used for surveying during the return trip. Anza was not fooled. He suspected that the friar wanted to see some of the new country by himself. "Make sure you get back in time," Anza once more warned him. "I shall go on without you if you delay."

But this time Father Garcés did not heed the Captain's words. In San Diego he met the already famous Father Junípero Serra and enjoyed his visit with him so thoroughly that he let the pack train proceed without him.

Anza was filled with dismay when he saw the pitifully small supplies his men brought back from San Diego. They were all that the mission had been able to spare. The tiny amount of beans, the maggot-infested maize and the jerked meat would barely feed the friars, let alone carry his men to Monterey. Without waiting for Father Garcés to come back, Anza decided that, with four of his own men and two soldiers from the mission, he would go on to Monterey. He left word for Father Garcés to take the rest of the expedition back to the supplies on the Colorado River and to wait for him there.

When Father Garcés arrived at the mission the following morning, Anza had already gone. The route from the San Gabriel Mission to the capital at Monterey led over country which had been traveled before and so was well marked. By pressing their mounts Anza and his party made the four hundred-mile journey in nine days.

At the presidio at Monterey a second celebration awaited them. Governor Fages' service in California was almost at an end. He was waiting to be relieved by Rivera, the new Governor. Although Fages agreed that the new overland trail could well be the long-sought supply route which would save the colony, it was not until that night, when Anza continued his journey south to the mission at Carmel, that he found a man with vision to match his own.

Now that his dream of blazing the overland trail had been accomplished, at once Anza began to make still further plans. Father Palóu, president of the missions in Father Serra's absence, was more than ready to furnish him with suggestions. Anza forgot his exhaustion as the two men sat up most of the night discussing ideas. One idea was for a fast mail route to be established between Mexico and California. Sonoran couriers could carry the post as far as the Colorado River where California couriers could pick it up. Another idea concerned a regular freight route between Sonora and California. Still a third had to do with the bringing of settlers to live in this new land. Anza liked this one best. Territory held only by presidios and missions would always remain a frontier. It took settlers, whole families, to build homes and raise children, to begin the chain of future generations that would someday turn a new land into a permanent country.

The following day, carrying mail for Mexico and accompanied by six Monterey soldiers who were to learn the route to the Colorado, Anza proceeded south. Once more the hard-riding Captain covered close to fifty miles a day. The journey was marked by one incident of importance. On the sixth day Anza met Father Serra who was traveling north to his home mission at Carmel. The Spanish Captain found Serra every bit as interested in the new overland trail as Father Palóu had been. But to Anza the satisfaction of finding a route across the desert was now a thing of the past. All his thoughts were concentrated on bringing colonists and supplies to California. This must be done quickly, before the mission Fathers starved to death or were forced to give up their slim hold on the new country.

On his return to the San Gabriel Mission, Anza found that Father Garcés and the others had followed the instructions he had left and had set out for the Colorado. Only Father Díaz remained behind. The friar was trying to master the use of the astrolabe with which he hoped to note latitudes on the return journey.

Such was Anza's haste to get on with his new plans that he rested only one day at the mission before starting homeward.

With good mounts and light packs, the small party climbed swiftly into the mountains. They had passed the crest and were dropping down toward the bleached white desert which glistened ahead, when Anza heard a startled whinny. Seconds later, three unmounted riding horses, obviously in wild panic, appeared. One traveled only a short distance, then went down in a clump of sagebrush. Anza looked up to see on the hillside above them several Indians who had apparently emerged from behind the shelter of some giant boulders. With a whistling sound, an arrow sped through the air and dropped only a few feet short of Anza's mount.

Leaping to the ground, the Captain seized his musket. The soldiers quickly followed his lead as still more arrows whistled around them. But instead of shooting at the men, the Spaniards suddenly realized that the Indians appeared to aim only at the horses.

The rocky hills echoed and re-echoed with the first volley of fire from Spanish muskets, but the skirmish was over almost as soon as it began. Already the Indians were fleeing. "After them!" Anza commanded the Monterey soldiers who spurred their mounts in pursuit.

While waiting for the soldiers to return, Anza ordered a check of the animals. Three had been wounded. The fleeing Indians (a small band of Serranos) were fleet of foot, but they had been no match for the mounted soldiers who soon came back, dragging several terrified braves with them.

With many motions the captives explained that they had not been aiming at the Spaniards but had hoped merely to drive off a few horses for food for their starving families. Moved to be lenient, Anza ordered the ringleader whipped, then turned loose with the rest after a stern warning not to interfere with future riders.

Anza's party had scarcely continued on its way before a young soldier, sent ahead as a scout, rode up to the Captain, motioning excitedly. He explained that he had found a crude message carved on a willow tree near the site of one of their former camps. The message could only have been left by Father Garcés but the young man had been unable to decipher it as he could not read.

Dismounting, Anza followed the soldier down a steep slope to the base of the tree. Moments later, his booming laughter filled the glade.

The message bore Father Garcés' initials. "Caution, Indians attacked horses here," it warned—a half-hour too late. "If I had read this first, that rascal ringleader wouldn't have got away with his life," Anza remarked. "The deceitful devil attacked the first party too."

It was May now and, as the travelers descended from forested mountain slopes into the desert foothills, blistering sunlight reflected from granite boulders and oven-hot sands. At their former camp site of San Sebastián on the edge of the desert, Anza found another message from Father Garcés. This one was longer and was sealed in a waterproof pouch. Instead of returning by way of the longer route, skirting the base of the Cocopahs, Father Garcés was heading directly into the desert toward the Deep Well of Little Water.

If Father Garcés could take the main party across the desert, then Anza was certain he could make it with his smaller group. At dawn he and his men left San Sebastián. The heat rising from the sands was like that from a giant furnace. As the sun rose higher the glare threatened to blind them, but the men pushed on in their attempt to keep up with their Captain who seemed to feel neither heat nor thirst. Delay, delay—always, to Anza, this was insufferable. To be moving, to be going somewhere, if only across a burning desert—this, to him, marked accomplishment!

By nightfall the travelers had reached the Deep Well of Little Water. Stopping only long enough to let men and animals drink, they continued on until eleven o'clock when Anza halted to allow a few hours' sleep. At dawn they were on their way again. Just twenty-five hours after they had left San Sebastián, the party reached the blue lagoon at Santa Olaya. It had been an unbelievable journey of ninety miles, almost non-stop, across the burning sands in the late spring heat. Here was Anza's answer to his defeat at the dunes. Never again would he or any party he commanded fear the unknown desert, though Anza admitted the route was one to be followed only by veteran soldiers. Colonists and heavily laden freight trains would still have to use the longer passage.

At Santa Olaya the encamped Indians greeted Anza joyously. From them he learned that Father Garcés and his men had reached Palma's camp. Relieved that his men were safe, Anza now had to worry only about his supplies. As the party started up the river, a growing crowd of Indians traveled along with them. Long before they reached the junction of the Gila, they encountered Palma heading south to meet them. The big chief was as friendly as before, but he had scarcely greeted Anza when he burst into tears.

Alarmed, at first Anza thought that some terrible catastrophe had occurred. But seconds later Palma set his mind at rest. His tears were for the muleteers and soldiers Anza had left behind to guard his supplies. Though Palma had pleaded with them to stay, only a short time after Anza and the main party had gone the men had deserted to return to Mexico. "They told me you had perished in the desert. They said that I would never see you again," Palma cried. "They laughed at me when I would not believe them. I would not believe that the wonderful God of my white brother would desert him." Motioning some of his braves closer, so that they could agree he was telling the truth, Palma began to recite a list of Anza's supplies. All were safe. When Anza's men had deserted, Palma had posted his own guards. Not one pack had been touched.

This time it was Anza who hugged the powerful chieftain. "You are indeed my brother," he said with feeling.

Anza's men could hardly make their way through the crowds of happy Indians jostling around them. The river was at flood stage now and nearly a third of a mile wide. Palma and his people, true to their promise, had constructed rafts which were already waiting on the bank. Thirty or forty naked braves leaped into the water to steady the first raft.

Scarcely had Anza dismounted to look over the situation, when he gave a startled grunt. Palma had seized him in his powerful arms and had lifted him into the air. Then, as another brave did the same thing to Father Díaz, Anza saw the Indians' intention. While his soldiers waded the few feet to the poised raft, Anza and the friar were carried so that not even their boots should get wet. At a shout from Palma, dozens of the strongest braves moved the raft into the current and started steering it across the river. From the banks nearly six hundred Indians, many of them women and small children, dove into the water and swam beside the rafts. The water was speckled with bobbing black heads. In case the raft sank or anyone slipped overboard, the Indians would be there to save their white brothers.

Father Garcés and the remainder of Anza's men waited to greet Father Díaz and Anza on the far side of the river. While his tired riders relaxed, Anza busied himself with plans for the return to Mexico. Instead of heading south across the Devil's Highway to Caborca, the way they had come, he decided to follow the Gila River east, then to turn south directly to Tubac. It would be over this easier river route that he would want to bring settlers and freight to California.

On May 13, the men started up the Gila River while Anza remained behind briefly in order to make certain that several head of cattle, which he was sending back to California, herded by six soldiers from Monterey, got safely across the river. While he was waiting on the bank with Palma, an excited messenger arrived. Some of the braves farther down the river, once more led by Palma's brother, the ugly Chief Pablo, were planning to kill the six soldiers as they returned home.

Anza had dealt with Pablo before. His predominant feeling was more one of annoyance at the delay than of fear, but he knew that if the Yuma Crossing was to be kept open for the Spaniards, no trouble could be tolerated among the Indians. He immediately sent a courier to bring back the men as a show of strength and ordered a party of two hundred Yuma braves under Palma to escort the Monterey soldiers to safety. When Palma returned with a message from the Monterey corporal that they were safely through enemy territory, Anza rewarded the chief with more clothes and his own baton as a symbol of his authority. Only then did Anza and his men set forth for home.

The incident had not seemed an important one, yet it bothered Father Díaz, who was wise for his years. "Indians are like emotional children; one day friends, the next enemies," the young friar told Anza. "We must build missions among them as soon as possible if we plan to bring people and supplies through their country to California. If they should ever decide to rise against us, it would take many soldiers to put them down again."

Anza nodded agreement. "That is one of the things I plan to discuss with Viceroy Bucareli in Mexico City. There can be no delay. We must have missions for the Yumas and settlers for California."

Father Garcés, jogging along beside Anza, made no comment. Eyes on the horizon, he seemed lost in thoughts of his own. He had shared Anza's dream of finding an overland route to California, but now Anza suspected he had small interest in missions and settlers. A strange, lonely man, he seemed to live only for distant horizons.

The travelers continued up the Gila Valley, passing through villages of friendly Cocomaricopas and Opas whom Father Garcés had visited on previous trips. Anza was not surprised when the Father decided to stay a while longer in one of the villages, then to visit others farther east before making his own way home. The friar refused a soldier escort. It was May when they said good-by to him. It would be July before the people of his own rather neglected little mission would see him, a gaunt figure, riding in from the desert on his bony horse. Likely an Indian servant, whom he would pick up along the way, would be walking behind, balancing a water olla on his head and carrying a stout stick to make the horse move faster when the good Father so desired.

Leaving the Gila River, Anza's party headed south to Tucson, through the land of the Pimas, most of whom lived under the authority of the Spanish. Here a message reached Anza, urging him to hurry. The Government inspector, Antonio Bonilla, was due to arrive any moment at Tubac. It had been a long time since Anza had worried about such civilized concerns as visits from inspectors. With Father Díaz and a few soldiers, he raced ahead of the main party. On May 26, four and a half months after he had left them, the brown adobe walls and green orchards of Tubac finally came into view.

How good it was to be reunited with Doña Ana and his three daughters! But the celebration in honor of his return came the following day when the main body of the expedition arrived. Every man, woman, and child, dressed in his finest clothes, lined the road leading to the main gates. After a Mass of Thanksgiving, there was feasting, dancing, and talking far into the night. Anza fell asleep in his own comfortable bed, planning the report he would soon be giving to the Viceroy in Mexico City.

Old Ghosts Return

ANZA'S DREAM WAS NOT to come true immediately.

By now the government inspector, Bonilla, had arrived at Tubac. Though a precise and persistent worker, Bonilla was not a man of vision. California was of no interest to him. His job was to inspect the border forts and see that there was no Indian trouble there. Now, the outpost at Terrenate was faced with one of the very uprisings he was supposed to prevent. Who better to put it down than Sonora's foremost Indian fighter, Captain Anza? Bonilla ordered Anza to Terrenate until such time as someone would be sent to relieve him.

As a soldier Anza had no choice but to obey. Sadly he bade farewell once again to Doña Ana and his friends at Tubac. He was to report for duty so quickly that he would not even have time to write to Viceroy

Bucareli until he had reached Terrenate. His state of mind was not helped when, with experienced eyes, he saw that the Indian troubles were very minor. All through the sweltering months of June, July, and August he waited restlessly for the relief Bonilla had promised. It did not come.

Though he was careful to hide his feelings from his soldiers, in private hours Anza gave way to a terrible depression. Despair filled his heart as he thought of the starving friars in California. He could not even be sure that reports telling of his successful expedition had reached the Viceroy in Mexico. If they had, apparently the dapper little official, who had promised so much in their earlier talks together, had already lost interest. Apparently, he didn't even care to receive Anza's personal report! During the nights when Anza tossed sleeplessly, despair would mount into helpless rage.

Of course Anza knew that it took months for messages to be carried back and forth, but undoubtedly he would have felt much better if he could have known that he was not the only man whose nights were sleepless.

While Anza's buckskin boots wore a path in the hard-packed earth floor at the remote outpost, Viceroy Bucareli's smaller, slipper-clad feet were wearing a path in the lush imported rug of his elegant Mexico City quarters. California was on his mind too. He had received the reports of the successful expedition. Couriers had delivered the letters written by Father Palóu and Governor Fages in California. The courier, Valdéz, had returned to Mexico City and had given a personal account of the trip. Father Díaz had lately been rewarded by being placed at the head of all the Pimería Baja missions but he had sent Bucareli his diary. By late July even wandering Father Garcés had returned home and sent along his scribbled notes. The Viceroy's feet paced faster. This was all very well, but where was Captain Anza, the one man he really wanted to see? Here he was, rushing ahead with plans for sending another expedition to California—and the man he wanted to lead it hadn't even bothered to report to Mexico City!

It was the end of August before Bucareli finally received Anza's letter from Terrenate explaining the delay. It was perhaps just as well that the inspector, Bonilla, was far away on the border and not present to witness the Viceroy's rage. A messenger was sent immediately to order that Anza be freed of duty. Still, it was November before Anza, at long last, reached Mexico City.

Along the way on the hard ride south, Anza rehearsed the arguments he would present to the Viceroy. Somehow he must rekindle Bucareli's interest in California and convince him he must send a new expedition to save the people of California. What a surprise awaited him in Mexico City when he found that no arguments were necessary. Already a second expedition had been planned and he had been chosen to lead it!

First, however, Bucareli insisted that Anza be given

the honors due him. By order already received from King Carlos in Spain, he was elevated to the rank of Lieutenant Colonel. Every soldier who had made the trip to California with him was granted a monthly bonus for the rest of his life.

For four days Anza enjoyed the social life of the capital; then he and Bucareli settled down to work. Beside the bronzed and rugged Anza, Bucareli, a slight, thin-lipped man with a fashionable taste in clothes, appeared something of a dandy. But he possessed a vision that surpassed even Anza's, coupled with an astonishing executive ability.

Already he had completed the first plans for the new expedition, needing only Anza's approval and suggestions. The purpose of the expedition would be threefold: to lead the first colonists overland to Monterey; to select the site for a new settlement on the shores of San Francisco Bay; and to explore the far side of the bay in order to find out if it was fed by a river. Not only would the expedition provide California with its first permanent colonists, but the northernmost settlement would also claim the great bay for Spanish use and prevent southward expansion by the Russians.

Agreeing quickly concerning this triple purpose, Anza and Bucareli turned to other details. Anza was to take with him thirty colonists and their families, along with the necessary muleteers and vaqueros to drive the pack mules, as well as a herd of cattle to supply food along the way and stock for the missions. Of the thirty colonists, it was decided that ten should be soldiers and their families from the frontier, already accustomed to hardships. The remainder would be recruited from the impoverished lands of Culiacán and Sinaloa where farmers, wiped out by recent years of drought, might be eager to make such a trip and start over again at government expense. In addition, Anza asked to take an escort of ten seasoned soldiers, who would later return with him to Mexico.

For his next in command Anza chose Lieutenant José Moraga of Fronteras and Sergeant Pablo Grijalva of Terrenate. For spiritual guidance, three priests were to accompany him. Father Garcés and Father Eixarch would remain with Palma's people at the Yuma Crossing to further their friendship, while Father Font, noted for his skill with surveying instruments, would accompany Anza all the way to California.

Anza was aware of mixed feelings of pride and awe. This time he would not be commanding just a simple expedition but what would be, in effect, a whole settlement on the move.

As the plans progressed, Bucareli's astonishing ability for organization became more and more apparent. Anza could see now why this man had risen to such a position of power. Not one tiny detail was beneath his attention. Since the colonists were being outfitted from the skin out by the government, lists ranged from the number of pairs of pants for each man down to women's undergarments and even hair ribbons. Those next weeks Anza felt more like a shopkeeper than an explorer as he rushed about, selecting buckskin for breeches, dress goods for skirts, even pots and pans.

He tried very hard to curb his impatience. He realized the importance of Bucareli's exacting plans. This was no journey with seasoned soldiers able to endure untold hardships. This trip would include women and small children too—the first settlers who could mean the future of California.

Even the Indians were remembered. Included for them were 350 pounds of tobacco and six large boxes of beads, mostly red. Bucareli even selected a personal gift to go to Chief Palma: a cloak trimmed with gold, buckskin jacket and breeches, and a cap with a feather cockade like those worn by the King's dragoons. Anza considered it typical of the dapper Viceroy that he should select a gift of fine clothes for the chieftain who was accustomed to going naked. But he thought Palma, now striding about with only his dangling medal and Anza's baton, would be pleased.

It was spring again before Anza bade the Viceroy good-by and set out, accompanied by the government commissary, Mariano Vidal, to begin recruiting his settlers. In the remote villages of Culiacán Anza set up the royal banner and opened his recruiting offices. The spirit of adventure was not dead, even in these quiet provinces far from the frontier. Often it was the wives who goaded their men into enlisting. Their pay began the very day they signed the roster. The drought had left them with almost nothing. A royal salary, new clothes for every member of the family, food, blankets, and household supplies, plus a fresh start in California—why would anyone hesitate at an offer like that?

Anza followed his supply trains north, selecting families as he went. It had been decided that Horcasitas, the capital of Sonora, would be their gathering point. Here the expedition would assemble and move together to Tubac, then head north to the trail along the Gila River. Anza hoped to get the expedition under way some time in September.

It was four hundred miles from Culiacán to Horcasitas, but Anza and his colonists arrived at the Sonoran capital well ahead of schedule, having picked up Father Font at his mission of San José de Pimas along the way. Doña Ana had come to Horcasitas to be with her husband. It was a time of happy reunion. There was even time for a little relaxation while Anza made the final check of supplies and animals. Because he was taking so many animals with him, some had been gathered at Horcasitas. Fresh horses would be picked up at Tubac. By the first of September Anza was able to give a grateful sigh. The long ordeal of preparation was almost over; in a few days the mammoth caravan would be on its way.

But he had forgotten his old enemies. On the night of September 7 tragedy struck at Tubac, though it was days later before a weary rider had traveled two hundred miles to gallop down the dusty streets of Horcasitas with the news.

As soon as the dust-streaked soldier was brought before him, the man's grim face told Anza that his news was bad. "Speak, man, Speak up!" he ordered.

"Apaches," the soldier gasped. "Four nights ago they raided the corrals, killed the guards and ran off the horses."

"The horses for the expedition!" Anza shouted, leaping from his chair. With the soldier's confirming nod, he seemed to be seeing history repeating itself. Leave it to his old enemies! Their raid on his stock had almost meant ruin for his first expedition. Would it mean the same now? This time he was responsible for not just thirty-four lives but for hundreds, including women and children.

He tried to control his surge of anger. "We were planning to start for Tubac in a few days. I suppose the soldier guard that is to escort us came with you."

The soldier dropped his eyes. "No, Colonel. The men do not have the mounts to come. The Apaches took the garrison horses as well as those for the expedition—five hundred in all."

Anza sank back in his rawhide chair. He must have time to recover from this second blow. Fortunately, he was accustomed to meeting misfortune with action. The next day he arranged for the necessary horses to be sent to the soldier escort at Tubac, while messengers were hastened to nearby forts and outposts to purchase or beg animals. Slowly the messengers returned with the best horses they could find, all poorer animals than Anza would have desired. He could only console himself with the fact that they were better than none.

Anza's troubles had only begun. Several nights later a stampede among the animals at Horcasitas cost him more horses. It was well into September now. The soldier escort arrived, but now Father Font was ill which meant another delay. Doña Ana, who with pride had watched her husband ride off many times before, suddenly was overcome with terrible forebodings of disaster. She begged him to delay even longer. Anza had given Viceroy Bucareli his promise that he would start in September. He was a man of his word. But on September 29, as he knelt in the plaza with the others, listening to Father Font's prayers for a safe journey, he had to struggle hard not to believe Doña Ana was right when she said that this was an expedition marked for trouble.

Later, as inexperienced muleteers struggled with slipping packs and families milled about trying to find their order of march, the confusion did nothing to relieve his fears. It took the huge party until four in the afternoon to get assembled and under way. Only two miles from Horcasitas it was time to unpack again and camp for the night. As Anza stared gloomily into his campfire he had to admit that the expedition, which had looked so magnificent on paper in Bucareli's offices in Mexico City, had gotten off to a sorry start.

Doctor Anza

IN THE MORNING BREAKING camp caused as much confusion as before. The muleteers were new and the animals untested. The loading process became a contest between man and beast. Two men were required for each pack animal. First the mule was blindfolded; then a soft sheepskin was thrown over its back to protect against chafing. On top of this came a saddle blanket and the leather pack saddle, fastened with a woven grass cinch. Now the load was added in three boxes, one on each side and the third on the animal's back. The two men pulled on the ropes on either side to tighten the pack. Last of all came a mat cover as protection against bad weather.

For the load to ride comfortably, cinches and ropes had to be tightened until the poor animals looked like hourglasses. The mules brayed so pitifully that some of the tender-hearted muleteers left the ropes too loose. During those first days packs continually fell off along the way.

And the families had their problems. Women had pots and utensils to pack each morning; shelters had to be taken down and wandering children located. These were robust farm and frontier people. Among them they had well over a hundred children, some families numbering as many as nine.

Even when the caravan was under way, Anza felt no lessening of the foreboding in his heart. Between the travelers and Tubac lay four hundred miles of Apache territory. Against attack Anza had a force of only twenty soldiers. He realized that the ten soldier-colonists who were traveling with their wives and children would be of little help. Though outfitted in helmets and leather armor, almost all rode with at least one young child clinging on behind. Others carried infants in their arms.

Anza gritted his teeth and doubled his advance party of scouts. The travelers were going to need all of the help of their patroness saint, the Lady of Guadalupe, just to reach Tubac, let alone to cover the long trail to California that lay beyond.

To add to his burdens Anza was not finding the warm feeling of brotherhood with Father Font that he had shared with Father Garcés. A stern-faced intellectual, Father Font lacked the robust health of the rangy Garcés. He still had not completely recovered from his recent illness. The fact that Anza, worrying over the pack animals, had forgotten to assign him a servant had already created a chill between the two men. Anza rode alone and silent, keeping his troubles to himself.

On the third day, as they were crossing a low range of desert hills, his worst fears were realized. A young boy galloped back to the caravan, whipping his sweating horse. "Indians! Indians over the hill. They're stealing our mules!"

As the word spread through the train, there was shouting coupled with frightened shrieks from the women. Whirling his horse about, Anza issued a torrent of commands. Soldiers handed down babies and children into the arms of their wives. The women and children were quickly enclosed in a protective circle while Anza ordered a party of scouts in the direction shown by the boy.

For a long time those who remained behind waited nervously. At last the scouts returned. They had covered the hills in every direction without finding Indians. It had been a false alarm. The boy must have seen a couple of their own muleteers chasing a runaway animal and had mistaken them for Indians.

With sighs of relief the people resumed marching order.

Twice during the journey the caravan had to stop for a day to wait for the lagging animals. Gradually, however, men and animals became accustomed to the routine. By the time they rode safely into Tubac on October 15, they were experienced travelers.

At Tubac they were joined by the remaining frontier families who were to make the trip to California. Anza was glad to see Father Garcés again. Knowing how the wandering friar enjoyed his solitude, he had been surprised when Father Garcés had asked that young Father Eixarch be sent with him to the Yuma Crossing where he was to work with the Indians. Anza had not betrayed his old friend to the Viceroy. He suspected that it was the husky young Eixarch who would be attending to the religious needs of the Yumas while Father Garcés indulged in his favorite pastime of exploring.

On October 23 the expedition, including two hundred and forty people and over a thousand head of horses and cattle, was ready to leave. Father Font said Mass, asking for Divine protection on the long ride ahead. He compared the travelers to the Israelites led by Moses to the Promised Land. His was an inspiring message but, as Anza knelt with the others in the dusty square, he wished the good Father had chosen some other text. He was just a rough frontier soldier, knowing only too well how little he possessed of wisdom and strength compared to the Biblical leader.

The Mass concluded, the people fell into the order of march. First came four soldier scouts; next came Anza with the three friars; then the settlers and soldier guard, followed by a rear guard under Lieutenant Moraga. Trailing behind were the pack animals, horses, and cattle. As the procession started away from Tubac, Father Font began reciting the Alabado, the people's voices joining with his as they would hereafter at the start of every day's march.

That night, when they had set up their tents and the brush and blanket shelters, the encampment resembled a small city. Father Garcés and Father Eixarch shared living quarters but Father Font and Anza each had a tent of his own. Anza's was round in shape so that it could be located easily among the others.

That first night Anza had barely settled down in front of his tent when Lieutenant Moraga rushed up to announce that he was needed immediately. Señora Felix, the wife of one of the colonists, was in childbirth. Summoning Father Font, Anza ordered the woman moved into the best tent available. In those days part of a commander's duties was caring for the medical needs of his men, but Anza's experience had consisted of binding up battle wounds and broken bones and he had had little experience as a midwife. A fine baby boy was added to the already good-sized Felix family, but in the early hours of the morning, in spite of Anza's efforts and those of the women helping him, the mother died.

His heart torn with grief, Anza stumbled from the tent to break the news to the anxious husband. One day on the trail—one death! It was hard to steel his soul against belief in ill omens. The colonists, most of them superstitious, soon left no doubt of how they felt. As the news of the death spread from camp to camp, a great sobbing arose. Anza could not blame the weeping women. For those from Culiacán, six hundred weary miles lay behind them and a thousand more ahead. How could they know that the fate of Señora Felix might not claim them too before the long trip was over?

While Father Font said prayers for the dead woman Anza sat alone, gazing into the fading firelight, his shoulders almost crushed with the weight of the terrible responsibility he was carrying. It was up to him to lead the way, choose the camp sites, guard against enemy attack, minister to the illnesses of his people, and keep them in good spirits. Had he undertaken a job too big for any one man?

In the morning Father Garcés rode on ahead with some soldiers and the body of the dead woman for burial at his Mission San Xavier. The others followed more slowly, riding with heads bowed as Father Font led them in reciting the Rosary.

It took two days for the main caravan to reach San Xavier and by the time they arrived spirits already were lifting. These were sturdy pioneer people accustomed to facing tragedy. A young mother offered to nurse the Felix baby with her own. Other women divided the Felix children among families which would not notice the addition of one more child. At San Xavier more prayers were said for the dead woman and Father Font performed three marriages. Already one had the choice between tears or laughter.

At the Indian village of Tucson, Anza had good news from his scouts. Recent rains had left ponds and watering places ahead of them in the desert all the way to the Gila River. Their hearts lightened, the members of the party moved on into unknown territory. They were leaving the land of the Christianized Pimas now. The next Indians they met would be savages.

To make sure that the Indians along the Gila River would be friendly to them, Anza sent ahead some Indian scouts. The following day a party of braves from the river villages rode out to greet them. Dismounting, their leader delivered a long speech. Not only were his people friendly but they had brought the Spaniards gifts. At a signal from the head man, the braves held out the recently taken scalps of two Apaches whom they knew to be the enemies of the Spanish. A startled silence fell over the party. Not wanting to hurt the Indians' feelings, Anza accepted the gruesome presents with thanks but tucked them out of sight of the women and children as quickly as possible.

By the time the Spaniards reached the river, a thousand Indians lined their way. Anza and the three Fathers had to shake the hand of everyone. Later, the four were escorted to a bower of branches the Indians had built for them. But, as the crowd continued to hang about, Anza knew what was wanted. He ordered his soldiers to open the packs of tobacco and beads. The Indians stumbled over each other in their eagerness to form a line, while Anza personally presented each with a gift. It was after dark before he had finished.

The following day the hand-shaking and gift-giving ceremony had to be repeated at the next village. Because of their diet and lack of cleanliness, the Indians had a very strong odor. The hand-shaking was an ordeal for delicate Father Font. However, Father Garcés, who lived like a savage himself, was at his happiest. Once again he brought out his treasured banner. Like the Yumas, these Indians shouted with joy at the beautiful picture of the Virgin and covered their eyes at the picture of the soul in agony. Father Garcés' long, solemn face shone with delight at their wise choice.

Now the weather turned cold and it began to rain. Though the colonists piled on more clothes, they were of little help. Soon everyone was riding with shoulders hunched against the wind, soaked to the skin. When a scout reported that there appeared to be a fine lake ahead, Anza ordered a halt so that the people could dry their garments and rest for the day.

But this proved to be an unfortunate decision. The next day more rain soaked through the shelters and put out fires. It was the King's birthday. To keep up the people's spirits and celebrate the occasion, Anza ordered a ration of aguardiente, the strong Spanish brandy. Noting Father Font's disapproval, Anza once again was aware of the differences between himself and the scholarly priest, who spent so much of his time alone in his tent writing in his diaries.

The following day Anza had more to worry about than a few drunken soldiers and the disapproval of Father Font. The party was unable to continue on because one of the women was seriously ill. That night several of the horses died and the next day more people were ill. Too late Anza realized that the pasturage and water of the lake were bad. By now so many people were ill that they named the lake Laguna del Hospital.

When the rain finally ceased and the sun appeared, the invalids were helped onto their horses and the travelers headed away from this lake of disaster. Even with the bad water behind them, animals continued to die and people to become ill. Now, because of the many who were sick, only a short distance could be covered each day. Far into the night Anza struggled from tent to tent, trying to nurse the sick with the limited knowledge he had. By now Father Font and Father Eixarch were ill too, but fortunately Father Garcés seemed immune to illness. At last some hot springs were reached. Here the women, for the first time in weeks, were able to do their washing and some of the ill recovered. But the colonists could not linger in the healthy surroundings of the mineral springs for long. California was still many miles ahead and it was creeping toward winter now.

Several nights later, in the chill darkness of their camp at the foot of the Mohawk Range, Anza was awakened by running footsteps outside his tent. Before he could throw aside his blankets a soldier burst through the flap. "Colonel, my wife. She needs you now! It has come on so quickly."

Anza called for someone to bring Father Font. As he plunged after the soldier, he was aware of a thin coating of icy frost crunching underfoot. His first thought was that the soldier's wife had been stricken with disease from the bad water. But when he burst into the crude blanket shelter and saw the two anxious women already attending her, he knew he had been summoned for another reason. For a moment his thoughts flew back to Señora Felix and his helplessness in attempting to save her. Behind him Father Font had pushed aside the curtains and was making the sign of the cross. Anza crossed himself too, then knelt beside the woman.

In the morning the word went out that all was well with both the mother and her new son. The Felix infant had taken his mother's place on the roster of the caravan. Now, with the addition of this new child, their ranks had actually increased. For the first time in weeks laughter raced through the camp. In spite of the bitter cold, and the fact that the caravan would have to delay a couple days while the mother recovered her strength, the birth seemed a good omen to everyone.

Only Anza was moody and thoughtful as he stared into his campfire. New worries oppressed his mind. It was well into November now and the travelers had not even reached the Yuma Crossing. If they did not hurry they would be crossing the California sierras in coldest winter. The caravan had not even reached the desert, the worst part of the trip, and already many of the best animals had been lost. Weakened by illness and burdened with women and children, they would be helpless if the Yumas for any reason decided to turn against them.

Anza was surprised when Father Font appeared like a thin wraith from the darkness to join him beside the fire. The priest managed an austere smile. "For a man who has safely nursed his people through illness and added a new life besides, you look very grave," he remarked.

"That is because my thoughts are grave ones," Anza replied. "The enemy I fear is not illness. It comes in human form."

Father Font looked puzzled. "You mean the Yumas? But I thought this Chief Palma was friendly."

"He was friendly when I last saw him," Anza agreed. "But I have had experience with Indians. It has been almost two years since then. There are some malcontents among Palma's tribe, principally a chief named Pablo. We must have the Yumas' help to cross the Colorado. With my people strong, I might bluff my way. But now, with our people weakened and many of our animals lost, I would be no match for Palma's strength were he to turn against me."

Anza waited. He half expected Father Font to remind him to place his trust in God as Father Garcés had always admonished him. Instead the priest shook his head thoughtfully. "It is a terrible burden for one man to carry alone. I shall pray for you that you find guidance in your decisions."

Anza felt strangely humble. This quiet, scholarly man was more observant than he had realized. As different as they were in personality, he felt the first faint stirrings of friendship with the priest. "I will be grateful for those prayers, Father," he said.

On the third morning the new mother was well

enough to mount her horse with her infant son cradled in her arms. As the travelers continued down the Gila River the going became more difficult. In places they crossed alkali flats where the burning dust stung their eyes. In other places they made their way through thickets of cactus and brambles that tore at their clothing. More of their starving, weakened animals died.

Anza sent word ahead to Palma that the caravan was approaching. Instead of coming to meet him as Anza had expected, the chief merely replied by messenger that his people were waiting.

On November 27, as they neared Palma's settlement, the soldier scouts sent back word that Indians were approaching. Minutes later Palma, leading a large party of braves, appeared over the crest of a hill. All the braves were mounted on their fleetest horses and most carried firebrands which they moved up and down to warm their glistening, naked bodies. Anza saw that Palma still wore the medal he had given him. Riding beside Palma, in the position reserved for his closest advisor, was his brother Pablo, hideously decorated with streaks of red and white mud, his pierced ears and nostrils bristling with sticks and feathers.

A sudden hush fell over the caravan. Motioning to his soldier guard to move in behind him, Anza rode forward alone.

The Yuma Crossing

As Anza approached, Palma dug brown heels into the sides of his horse and moved to meet the chief. Both braves and waiting settlers were completely silent as the pair dismounted.

Then a wide smile came over Palma's proud face. He threw himself forward, his muscular arms seizing Anza's shoulders. His great dark eyes were wet with emotion. "My brother! My brother, you have returned!" he cried.

A heavy weight seemed to roll from Anza's chest. He returned the embrace with affection. When Palma presented him with a small pouch filled with dried beans, he accepted it as though it had been a gift of diamonds. Though of little value, he knew it must have some symbolic meaning for the Indians.

Palma's welcome did not stop with Anza. The chief quickly turned to the long line of colonists. Father Font was caught by surprise as the husky Indian almost pulled him off his horse. After that, Palma clasped Father Garcés and Father Eixarch to him, then went down the line, taking every man, woman, and child in his arms. If some would have preferred a less enthusiastic greeting, they were wise enough to say nothing. With a gentle but curious finger, Palma even pried open the blankets and pressed his brown cheek to that of the new baby.

At last he strode back to Anza. "My people! These are my people—the ones you promised would come to live among us! What lands you want will be yours. I pray to your God and my prayers are answered!"

Suddenly the cold weight returned to Anza's heart. It was plain that Chief Palma believed the colonists had come to build a mission and live among his people. He glanced toward Father Font for help. None came, unless perhaps the silent, stern-faced Father was praying that Anza be given the right words in answer.

"I am sorry, my brother." Anza put his hand on Palma's shoulder. "These people come only to visit and bring you gifts. They must go on to California where they are badly needed at our missions there. Later our great Viceroy will send others to build the mission for your people."

Palma's smile faded. "What does your Viceroy care about a poor Indian like me?" he said angrily.

"The Viceroy does care a great deal," Anza replied.

"He thinks so much of you he sent a special gift just for you." Anza quickly ordered the packs opened so that he could present Palma with the uniform sent by Bucareli. Delighted, Palma seemed to forget his resentment. "I wish I could see this great man!" he cried.

"You can," Anza assured him. "When I return from California, if you wish I will take you back to Mexico with me. You can meet the Viceroy and ask him yourself for a mission among your people."

In his joy over the prospects of such a trip, Palma's good humor returned. Not to be outdone, Pablo dismounted and also hugged Anza. To spare the rest of the party from being embraced again, Anza encouraged Pablo to make a speech.

While the Indians rode ahead with the scouts to help select a camping site for the night, Father Font fell in beside Anza.

"Well, what do you think of our Chief Palma?" Anza asked the Father with a smile.

To his surprise, Father Font's thin lips pressed together. "A simple, childlike creature. He follows you about like a dog. In my opinion his brother Pablo is a man with more spirit."

Anza glowered at the Father. Once again, here was a wide difference of opinion. Pablo might appear to have mended his ways since the Spaniard's last trip, but Anza was not prepared to trust him. He wondered for a moment if Father Font might not be jealous of his friendship with Palma.

The following day the colonists crossed the Gila River to camp on the strip of land between it and the Colorado. Here many of the Yuma Indians came to greet them. They built a thatched shelter for the leaders of the caravan and showered their visitors with gifts of vegetables and fruit. The most welcome was the three thousand watermelons which the Indians had preserved by burying them in the sand in preparation for this occasion.

Even as he joined in the celebration, Anza was already plotting the crossing of the Colorado. From Palma he learned that the ford used on the previous trip had been washed away by changes in the channel. When Anza suggested rafts, he was told that at this time of year the water was too cold for the Indians to swim his people across as they had before. Chief Palma seemed unconcerned. He was in no hurry to have the visitors leave.·

Anza was secretly impatient. They still had far to go. The next morning, taking one soldier with him, he set off upstream, determined to find a ford. At this time of year the way was almost blocked with thickets of brush and bogs where the horses struggled in mud above their fetlocks. In two hours they had covered less than a mile. Then, as the two men pressed through one of the worst of the thickets, Anza thought he heard a change in the roaring of the river. Dismounting, he clawed through the brush and saw that the river divided into three channels in order to flow around two islands. Here, where they could cross in stages between the islands, he decided to make the ford. He sent the soldier to bring men with axes to start clearing a trail; he himself rode into the water to test the footing and current.

In the morning everything, including supplies and animals, was moved to the site of the three channels. Anza had planned the crossing with all the care of a military maneuver. Women and children were mounted on the tallest horses and the packs were reduced to a single bundle instead of the usual three. Ten men were ordered into the water downstream from the crossing in case anyone should be swept away. The cattle and loose animals would be driven across last of all.

To the colonists from the desert country of Sonora and Culiacán, the muddy Colorado was an awesome sight. It was the largest river they had ever seen, three to six feet deep and nearly four hundred yards across. Many were terrified. "We will all drown!" "We will be swept away!" frightened voices protested everywhere.

Pretending not to hear, Anza motioned the crossing to begin. Taking up the reins of one of the horses, he led the first woman and child into the water. His scornful silence left no doubt in anyone's mind—they would cross the river and go on to California. Any who did not care to do so could stay with the Yumas or find their own way back to Culiacán. Grumbling stopped. Grim-faced men kicked their horses into the water. Terrified women clutched the children and turned the reins over to the soldiers who were leading their horses.

Anza had crossed with the first riders. Now he returned to assist the others. A line stretched from bank to bank now, some horses still feeling their way on hard bottom, others swimming with riders clinging to their necks. From one of the islands, a rider, holding a little girl in front of him, urged his horse into the river. Suddenly the horse plunged into a deep hole. The man's head appeared above water almost instantly, but a shout of alarm went up from the bank as the child was swept from his arms. She whirled downstream, small arms extended. One of the waiting guards grabbed for her but missed. The next guard plunged his mount forward into the swirling current. A great cry went up. The second guard hoisted the child high in the air above his head. Unharmed but shivering, she was handed to the bank to be carried across by someone else.

Anza had expected grumbling among the water-shy colonists, but once he had made it plain they must follow or be abandoned, they were obedient. To his disgust, it was Father Garcés and Father Font who caused the most trouble.

In spite of Anza's assurance that the water was no more than six feet deep in places, Father Garcés refused to trust himself to a horse. "You can't swim, the water is over the Indians' heads, and the wind is not going to blow you across like thistledown!" Anza snapped at him angrily.

Without deigning to reply, Father Garcés motioned haughtily to three braves. He stiffened his body and the Indians lifted him over their heads. Anza held his breath as the braves struggled to keep their footing. The water rose higher and higher around them. Father Garcés, lying prone with hands clasped on his chest, gazed quietly heavenward; no doubt his faith in God as well as in three grim-faced Indians carried him safely to the other side.

Father Font had been mounted on one of the tallest horses. The moment the horse stepped into the water he complained that he felt light-headed. Anza ordered three Indian servants to assist him, one to lead the horse, the others to support the Father, one man on each side. In spite of this assistance, the friar was soaked to the knees.

"A fine thing this will be for my fever," he complained. "I notice it is never *I* who gets the good animals."

On the far bank Anza had had fires built and a little brandy made ready for those who were wettest and coldest. Father Font consented to dry his legs by the fire but gazed disapprovingly at the brandy.

Not one person was lost during the crossing. Even the pack animals crossed safely with only one pack getting wet when a mule temporarily lost its footing. By some unfortunate coincidence, this was the pack that contained Father Font's vestments. "I notice you were able to find a strong mule for the barrel of aguardiente, but only a weak one for the vestments of the church," he told Anza peevishly.

Anza said nothing but that tiny spark of friendliness

he had felt toward the Father was rapidly extinguishing itself. It was enough to plan the crossing without having to listen to complaints. For fear he might retort angrily, he turned on his heel and strode away.

It was late in the afternoon before the last animal was safe on the opposite side of the river. That night there was dancing beside the campfires and Palma strode about, proudly wearing his elaborate blue-and-gold uniform. Though the chief had been singled out for special attention, Anza did not forget the other Yumas. The following day he lined up the rest of the tribe and gave tobacco to the men and beads to the women.

Anza was anxious to move on, but first there were several duties that had to be discharged here beside the Colorado River. He arranged the signing of a peace treaty between Palma and the chiefs of the Opas, who had accompanied the chief from their villages on the Gila River. He sent scouts ahead to search for new water holes on the desert. Father Garcés and Father Eixarch were to remain here to work with the Indians, so a cabin site must be selected and the cabin actually built for them before departure.

On the afternoon following the successful river crossing Anza was helping his men fell trees for the building when he was called back to camp. Three of the colonists had become gravely ill. Anza would try to nurse them back to health while Lieutenant Moraga continued directing the work on the cabin. Luckily, three days later all of the members of the caravan were well enough to resume the march. Anza said good-by to the two priests. The cabin was not quite finished but, in addition to supplies, Anza was leaving servants to help them as well as several interpreters.

Before the moment of departure Anza summoned Palma and Pablo to his tent. He instructed them to take care of the two padres. "I will watch over them as though they were my brothers," Palma promised.

As for Pablo, he leaped about with wild shouts and gestures, showing how he would scalp anyone who so much as said a cross word to the Fathers. Shocked by his bloodthirsty glee, Father Font suggested that flogging an offender would perhaps be enough. Apparently Pablo had never heard of this punishment. The idea amused him so much that he rolled on the ground, beating his sides and kicking dust over everyone. There was a sly twinkle in Anza's eye as he caught Father Font's look of disgust. In one short week the Father had changed his opinion about the ugly, boasting chief and was going to be as glad as Anza was to be rid of him.

The farewells outside Anza's tent were just over when a soldier brought word that the scouts had returned. The men had not found any new water holes on the desert but there was water in their former stopping places at Signal Mountain and the Deep Well of Little Water. They had also found what appeared to be a trail directly through the dunes.

For several moments Anza paced beside the tent, struggling to make his decision. The longer route around the base of the Cocopah Range would be the safest one. But it was December now. Every day of delay brought that much closer the possibility of being blocked by snows while crossing the mountains beyond the desert. "We will go directly through the dunes," he said finally.

"Colonel, that will be a hard trip for the women and infants!" one of the scouts blurted.

Anza gazed at him coldly. "We will go through the dunes," he repeated.

Sand And Snow

WINTER HAD COME NOW. As the caravan left Palma's village and started down the river toward Santa Olaya, the last friendly oasis before plunging into the desert, the settlers found need for all the clothing the government had given them. One garment was added on top of another until most of the women were wearing every skirt and petticoat they owned. Children were so wrapped in blankets and shawls that they resembled woolly sheep. Many of the people were ill, but they clung to the backs of their horses and tried to keep up with their companions.

It took two days to reach the long, curving lagoon of Santa Olaya. Here the Indians gave the travelers more of the watermelons which had been buried in the sand. However, the real treat was the fresh fish the men caught in the lagoon.

At this time of year there was good pasturage around the lake. So that their weakened animals could build up strength, Anza ordered a layover of several days. Knowing that the human travelers would need all their courage for the ordeal ahead, Anza ordered a small ration of aguardiente in spite of Father Font's forbidding looks.

There was singing and dancing around the campfires that night. Unfortunately, the priest was right about the aguardiente. A few celebrated too zealously, including Anza's cook. Anza and the Father had to go without their dinner.

The following morning, after he had said Mass, Father Font hurried to the circular tent. Barely waiting for Anza to greet him, he began an angry tirade. "Why do you purposely give these people drink when you know they'll get drunk?"

"I do not give it to them for that purpose!" Anza protested. "I cannot help it if a few misbehave. For the others it is a small enough treat, considering the hardships they have endured."

Father Font drew himself up haughtily. "If drunkenness is a sin, contributing to drunkenness is even more sinful. Ignorance might be an excuse, but I do not believe you are ignorant of what you do."

Knowing that the priest was not well and had gone without his dinner the previous evening, Anza admitted that Father Font had reason to be angry. But the commander had far more pressing worries than a drunken cook. It was all he could do to control his own hasty temper. "I do the best I can," he snapped.

Apparently Father Font did not think Anza sufficiently repentant. With an angry sniff he left the tent.

When he had gone a terrible loneliness filled Anza's heart. He needed Father Font's spiritual counsel, yet somehow the two men had never succeeded in becoming friends. Camped here at Santa Olaya, it was not too late for Anza to change his mind about taking the expedition through the dunes. But once they had started into the desert there would be no turning back. It was a terrible decision for a man to make alone. He thought wistfully of Father Garcés and the warm comradeship that had allowed them to share problems and troubles on their previous trip.

As though in answer to his thoughts, there were sudden shouts outside. Unbelievably, brown robes swinging, there was Father Garcés riding into camp on his bony horse. Anza rushed to greet his old friend. He had been right in his surmise about who would be ministering to the spiritual needs of the Yumas. Barely waiting to get young Father Eixarch started on his new duties, Father Garcés had headed toward his beloved wilderness.

His homely face creased in a broad smile, the friar sank cross-legged to the ground. With a pointed twig he drew a rough map in the damp earth. First he planned a brief visit to the mouth of the river. Later he hoped to explore up the river where, among the Indians, he might learn of a route to California north of the great desert. "Perhaps I may even meet you in

Monterey," he told Anza.

Anza did not need to be reminded that finding a northern route beyond the desert had long been a dream of the lanky friar. Suddenly Anza felt much better. If Father Garcés, armed with only faith and a silken banner, could set out confidently into a wilderness, surely he, Anza, could find the self-assurance to choose the right route across the desert.

Still determined to lead his people directly across the dunes, Anza planned the assault with the thoroughness of a military maneuver. In order to make the most of the scanty water holes, the colonists would be divided into three groups, traveling twenty-four hours apart. Anza, with Father Font, would lead the first group. Sergeant Grijalva would follow with the next group, while the third party under Lieutenant Moraga would bring up the rear. The cattle and the vaqueros would travel separately, making the crossing without water.

As a final precaution Anza went among the settlers, instructing them to fill their water skins and to go into the fields and cut bundles of grass which they would carry tied to their saddles. The water could save their lives; the grass might save the horses. Anza himself and Father Font were not exempt from this order. On the morning of December 9, the day chosen for the start into the desert, they too rode with bundles of grass tied to their saddles.

The bitter cold was growing worse. Packs were opened and every available garment was added to those the people were already wearing. Tears mingled with

well-wishes as Anza, Father Font, and twelve families
said good-by to the others and started away from Santa
Olaya under ominously gray skies. There was no singing. Everyone needed to save his strength. For seventeen miles they rode through a sandy wasteland that
supported only small clumps of cactus and salty, low-
growing brush. Calling attention to occasional piles
of shells in the sand, Father Font pointed out that
years ago this desert must have been under some great
arm of the sea. Anza, his eyes on the horizon, did not
hear him. Only one thought was in his mind—*water*.
At three in the afternoon he called a halt near one of
the former camp sites, where the men presently found
water by digging a hole in the arroyo.

The night was cold and in the morning the skies
were even more heavily overcast. That day progress
was much slower. The travelers passed the Deep Well
of Little Water which had saved the lives of Anza and
his men on their first expedition. Now it contained so
little water that there was no point in stopping. That
night they camped in a sandy wash where there were
a few dead mesquite trees which furnished wood for
their campfires. There was no water or grass. The
families portioned out water from their containers and
fed the bundles of grass to their animals. Two days into
the desert, the worst leg of their journey still ahead of
them, and they had already used their emergency
supplies!

Long before dawn Anza arose to help his men feed
the horses. Ahead lay the hardest lap of the trip, thirty-

five miles across the dunes to the wells at the base of the Impossible Mountain. It was here that Anza and his soldiers had been turned back before. What would happen with women and children in tow?

When the first light of the sun began to show in the east, Anza sent a party of soldiers ahead to open the wells at the mountain. By seven o'clock the entire party was mounted and on its way. The advance soldiers at once discovered a trail that skirted the worst of the dunes, but sands were constantly shifting. Even with the new and easier trail, there were places were the party had to struggle hard to make any progress. Soon the strongest men dismounted and continued on foot. It was wise to save the strength of the horses in case they would be needed later for the women and children. However, by now many in the party were so numb with cold that they could not have walked even if their animals had fallen.

This time Anza did not ride at the head of the column with the scouts and Father Font. Instead, he seemed to be everywhere at once—forging ahead, circling the caravan, riding down the line time after time to give a word of encouragement to those who were faltering. Somehow he kept them going, plodding on mile after weary mile. Darkness had fallen when at last they sighted firelight in the distance beside the Impossible Mountain.

The soldiers Anza had sent on ahead had lighted campfires and had dug six wells in the sand. But the travelers' troubles were far from over. No sooner had the thirsty people started drawing up water than the wells began to go dry. To Anza the thought that he had brought his people safely across the dunes only to have them die of thirst beside the Impossible Mountain was more than he could bear.

"The wells cannot go dry! I will not let them go dry!" he shouted. Tearing off his jacket and leather vest, he seized a shovel and leaped into one of the shallow wells. Dressed only in a thin shirt, his muscular arms flashing, he began to dig like an insane man. Damp sand flew over his shoulder, splashed his fine shirt, clung in glistening drops to his black beard.

His frenzy spread to the others. Men who, moments before, had been so tired they had scarcely been able to walk, leaped into the other wells. "Dig! Dig! Dig!" Their voices became a chant. When a man's strength gave out his comrades hauled him from the pit and another took his place. At last water began to flow again.

But their troubles were not over. It was necessary to keep the men digging in shifts all through the night in order to keep water flowing. Water for the animals had to be brought up slowly, one basketful at a time. It was ten o'clock the following morning before every animal in the caravan had been given a share. At noon Anza ordered man and animal alike, whether exhausted, ill, or dying, away from the wells and into the desert. By now Sergeant Grijalva and the second party would be starting into the dunes. Tonight their lives might depend on the water the first party left behind.

The weary caravan could not travel far. After covering only a short distance, Anza ordered a halt. Few put up tents for the night. Most families, huddled together for warmth, simply slept on the sand.

Yet in the morning the travelers awoke with renewed hope. In spite of dark skies and mounting clouds, they could see the edge of the desert ahead and the blue, snow-capped sierras of California.

At three that afternoon the caravan reached the foot of the mountains and the clear fresh water of San Sebastián.

Anza's original plan of march had not called for the three separate parties to be reunited until they had reached one of the really good springs in the mountains. However, seeing the snow above them and considering the hardships his group had undergone in the desert, Anza decided to wait for the other two parties here. There was plenty of firewood. Soon tents had been put up and food set to cook over many campfires. The main problem that faced them now was the cold. Early in the morning it began to snow. To those who had never experienced a snowfall, the cold white blanket that covered everything was almost terrifying. Later in the day the snow turned to a steady rain.

Father Font spent most of the day in Anza's tent which offered the best protection against the weather. The commander was not in the mood for conversation. A dozen times he left the tent to walk to the edge of the camp. He stood looking across the desert. This was the day Sergeant Grijalva was due to arrive. Where was he? Surely he should be able to see the sergeant and his party in the distance.

Shortly after noon a cry went up from the sentries. Anza and the other men rushed to the edge of the camp. Something was moving far out on the desert.

This was not Sergeant Grijalva and his companions. Coming toward them was a herd of cattle. Three days without water, the creatures had scented the springs and were heading for San Sebastián at full stampede, lowing and bellowing as they ran! Anza's men rushed to mount horses in order to ride to the help of the weary vaqueros who rode toward them. A number of cattle had died or been abandoned along the way, but, though they had run out of both water and provisions, the vaqueros were in good spirits.

The stampede was quickly controlled. Long after the cattle had settled down to graze, Anza stood staring into the desert. Behind him the evening campfires flickered to life like fireflies, but nowhere in the darkness ahead could he see an answering flicker of light. Sergeant Grijalva and the second party must be out there somewhere!

By morning a number of the waterlogged cattle and mules had died from exposure, but the animals did not worry Anza now. What had happened to the people? He did not have to worry long. Shortly after dawn horsemen were spotted on the desert. By noon Sergeant Grijalva had reached the camp. His people had lost a number of animals and had been delayed by the snowstorm. They had suffered horribly from the cold. Some were so stiff with the cold that they had to be lifted from their horses and carried like logs to the fires. But not one life had been lost.

"What about Moraga? He must be only a short distance behind you," Anza questioned Grijalva when the sergeant had thawed sufficiently to talk. Since Grijalva's party had been delayed by a day this was also the day the third party should arrive.

The sergeant shook his head. "For all our stops and delays, we never saw Moraga. Always I kept looking behind. Nothing—" He raised his hands helplessly. "He has run into trouble too."

Anza resumed his vigil at the edge of the camp but Lieutenant Moraga and the third party did not arrive that day nor the following. When, on the third day, there still was no sign of the missing party, Anza sent soldiers with twenty horses into the desert to investigate.

At noon a sharp-eyed boy spotted horsemen in the distance. The lost had been found! Lieutenant Moraga's people had suffered even more than the others. Fifteen of their animals had died along the way. They had been caught by the snowstorm in the sand dunes. Not one of them had escaped frostbite. The young lieutenant himself had such a terrible cold in his head that he had gone completely deaf. But once again not one life had been lost.

Anza gathered his lieutenant into his arms. "You are alive! Alive!" he cried, unmindful of the fact that the young man could not hear him. Though he could not hear, Lieutenant Moraga was able to join with the others in a lively fandango that night around the campfire. One more terrible ordeal was behind them. There was good reason for singing and dancing. Anza did not protest when the merriment continued far into the night.

"Better they should be on their knees giving thanks to God that they did not perish like their poor animals," Father Font commented severely.

Anza stared into the small campfire the two men were sharing. "They are only human," he said.

"And so, I have noticed, are *you*," Father Font commented dryly.

Sierra Christmas

AFTER A SHORT REST at San Sebastián, Anza gave orders to move on into the mountains. By now the carcasses of animals from the caravan lay strung across the desert like grim milestones reaching all the way back to Santa Olaya. Each morning during their stay at San Sebastián a few more cattle and mules had been found dead. Anza had ordered the cattle butchered, but in most cases the meat was sour and not fit for eating.

More serious was the loss of riding animals. Fortunately, enough of the supplies had been used so that Anza ordered pack saddles removed from twenty of the mules; these would serve as mounts. Even so, when they were ready to start, for the first time some of the party must travel on foot.

Though they were to head into the mountains now, for a few days the travelers would be climbing through desert foothills covered only with cactus, rocks, and sparse brush. That night they made a dry camp on a barren flat beyond an old salt-encrusted lake. The following night they camped in a rocky valley where there was a small well in the sand.

Long before they had watered all their thirsty animals the well began to go dry. Once again Anza seized a shovel and began digging. His men working with him, they soon deepened the hole to six feet. Though they continued digging more wells far into the night, none filled with water. For a second night the thirsty animals went without a drink.

The clouds had disappeared now, but, with clear, star-bright skies overhead, the night seemed even colder. Many people, unable to sleep, huddled about the fires. Anza's long years of military training made it possible for him to snatch a few hours' rest even under the worst of conditions. At midnight he was awakened by shouting and the sounds of a commotion.

Anza's keen ears quickly told him what was happening. There was no mistaking the rumbling sound that reverberated through the night. It was the sound of hundreds of hoofs already fading into the distance. Crazed with thirst, once again the cattle had broken from the vaqueros and were stampeding toward their last watering place, two days behind them at San Sebastián.

There was nothing to be done until daylight. At dawn Anza sent Sergeant Grijalva and some of the vaqueros to find the cattle. Without a supply of water it would be folly for the others to wait for their return. The rest of the party packed their belongings and set forth into the mountains. Since leaving San Sebastián they had left behind them a new trail of dead or abandoned animals. More members of the party were walking now. It was no longer possible to cover much distance in a single day, but by afternoon, when Anza called an early halt, they had reached their first mountain water. From now on water would be no problem.

The caravan rested a day, awaiting the return of the vaqueros with the cattle. By nightfall there was still no sign of Sergeant Grijalva. The following morning Anza sent soldiers to look for him. It was evening again when sounds in the distance told them that the wanderers were returning. Anza hurried to a small knoll where he could greet the men as they came into the canyon. His heart sank when he saw the pitiful remnant of the herd which the vaqueros were driving before them.

"Where are the rest of the cattle? Did you leave them behind to regain their strength at the springs? Without a guard the Indians may steal them." Anza's voice was filled with anxiety as he addressed the sergeant.

Grijalva shook his head. "These are all that are left, Colonel." He explained that some of the exhausted cattle, unable to keep up the pace of the stampede, had halted after only a short distance. These were the animals he and the vaqueros had driven back. The others, fifty head in all, had continued all the way to San Sebastián. By the time the sergeant and his men had caught up with them, all were dead. "If only the vaqueros had kept a better watch! If only I had not waited until dawn to go after them," he concluded bitterly.

"No one is at fault," Anza comforted the man. However, his cheerful words concealed a heavy heart. These were the cattle that were to have supplied the missions of California. To have brought them all this distance, only to lose them a few days away from the green pastures on the other side of the sierras, was indeed a cruel blow.

During the next few days, as the party climbed higher into the mountains, Anza rode frequently down the long straggling line of march. The main object of his concern was the bulky figure of a woman, clinging stubbornly to the back of her plodding mule. Before long there would be a new member of the caravan. The other women whispered that Señora Gertrudis was in much misery, but each time the commander spoke to her she shook her head and even managed to smile. Of sturdy stock, she refused to halt the party until it was absolutely necessary to do so.

At two o'clock that afternoon it was Anza who ordered a halt. Several head of cattle which had died that day were dragged into camp and butchered. The meat was distributed to every family. Since it was December 24 and Christmas Eve, he ordered a ration of aguardiente for everybody. So that Father Font would not be too disapproving, he stood in front of his tent and called in a loud voice for everyone to hear, "See that you behave yourselves. Any man caught drunk outside his tent will be punished."

Soon the Father and Anza had other things to worry about. It seemed strangely fitting that the third and last baby to join the expedition should be born on Christmas Eve. By now Anza had become quite proficient as a midwife. Shortly after eleven o'clock, when it was announced that mother and son were well and healthy, shouts of joy went up from the campfires. No one felt like sleeping. In spite of the rain that had begun to fall, there was singing and dancing far into the night.

Both because of bad weather and the new baby, Anza delayed the march another day. Most of the people attended Mass. When Father Font scolded them for their revelry on Christmas Eve they looked so remorseful that even he relented and wished them all the blessings of Christmas.

Next day Señora Gertrudis insisted that she and her young son were well able to travel and the colonists set out toward the pass. Late in the afternoon they were startled by a low rumbling in the earth. The ground seemed to shudder. But within seconds the small earthquake was over. Instead of being frightened, the people took this as a good omen. They had almost reached the pass. Tomorrow they would descend into the green valleys of California. God must have shaken the earth in recognition.

But on the morrow, after they had actually crossed the San Carlos Pass, for many happiness turned to fear. They had climbed high enough now so that the snow fields reached almost to the trail they were following. Clouds blotted out the valleys below. In every direction all one could see were the snow-capped peaks of other mountain ranges, rising above a gray sea of mist. To people from the warm regions of Mexico the snow was an awesome sight. Some of the women began to cry from both homesickness and fear. Over and over again Anza had to assure them that California was not a land of snow, that in the valleys below they would soon find sunshine again.

As the party descended into the green, oak-shaded valley, spirits began to revive. The long journey was at last drawing to a close. There was plenty of water and grass and Anza sent a rider ahead to the San Gabriel Mission to bring back spare horses.

To these people from the arid desert country this was a strange and beautiful land with its live oaks, wild grapevines, roses, berry bushes, and huge blooming sunflowers. To Father Font it was particularly appealing. The climate and the countryside reminded him of his boyhood home in Spain. "This is truly the land that should be called New Spain," he repeated over and over. Forgetting his aches and pains, he was as eager as a boy as he rode beside Anza, pointing out rosemary plants or a certain variety of snails known to the Old World. He even dismounted to gather some crisp salad greens for their dinner. For a few pleasant days the men almost forgot their differences.

Crossing the sierras, the travelers had noticed Indians in the distance from time to time, but few had

come close. In only one or two instances had Anza
been able to persuade any of them into camp, even to
receive presents. He was puzzled for on the first expedition all had seemed eager for gifts. He had finally
dismissed the matter, deciding that the Indians were
frightened by the number of people. He could not
know that this truly was an evil omen.

On the last day of the old year the settlers reached
the Santa Ana River. Anza had once before encountered
difficulty crossing this stream; again this time it was
running full and swift. The river was not wide but
very deep and the current flowed at such speed that
everything was swept before it. Camp was set up and
presently Anza inspected the single cottonwood log,
all that remained of his former bridge.

In the morning he ordered another cottonwood cut
down and logs laid beside the log already there. One
by one the women and children were helped across the
slippery makeshift bridge. After that the packs were
carried over. However, when the animals had to swim
the ford, a bull and a riding horse were carried away
and drowned.

Before the crossing had been completed, what looked
to be a large party of horsemen appeared in the distance. As it drew closer, Anza saw that there were only
three riders, the soldiers he had sent ahead to the
mission, but they were driving seventeen fresh horses.
At the sight a joyous shout went up from the whole
company.

But the soldiers brought bad news. There had been

an Indian uprising at the San Diego Mission and Father
Jaume had been killed. Only by a miracle had Father
Fuster and four mission guards escaped with their lives.
The corporal in command at the San Gabriel Mission
dared not leave his post to greet Anza for fear the revolt
would spread in his absence. Meanwhile, Governor
Fernando de Rivera was riding south, with soldiers
from Monterey, to put down the uprising. Anza knew
now why the Indians in the mountains had avoided
his party. It did not take long for Indian runners to
spread news from one tribe to another.

With fresh horses it took only a few days to reach
San Gabriel. Since Anza's last trip the mission had
been moved from its old site beside the river to a fertile
valley a short distance to the northwest. Because both
people and animals were extremely tired, the travelers
camped their last night at the old site, but the next
morning, January 4, 1776, they had been on the road
only two hours when they saw ahead the grazing sheep
and the adobe and log buildings of the new mission.

By now Governor Rivera and his troops had arrived.
The Governor and Father Paterna came down the road
to meet the new arrivals. Fathers Cruzado and Sánchez
tolled the mission bells. The mission guards fired a
welcoming volley from their muskets. Though the settlers were sorely bedraggled and half-starved, they were
a welcome sight to the lonely men of the mission. Many
a rough soldier's eyes filled with tears as he saw the
thin, wasted bodies of small children.

Monterey still lay ahead, four hundred miles to the

north, but the expedition had made it safely to California.

Governor Rivera, a stiff, arrogant-looking man with brooding dark eyes, was eager to talk with Anza. "You could not have arrived at a better time," he told the commander when the two of them were at last alone. He went on to give details of the uprising at San Diego. Six hundred Indians were supposed to have taken part. It appeared that the revolt had been planned very carefully. The Indians had waited until several of the priests and most of the soldier guard had gone north to found a new mission at San Juan Capistrano before launching the night attack in which they had murdered Father Jaume and looted the storerooms. Now, the Governor's plan was to go south, put down the uprising, and, as an object lesson, find and punish every participant in the rebellion.

The man paced the floor restlessly. "Yes, it is good you have come," he repeated. "I doubt if my soldiers alone will be strong enough to punish these sayages properly. I will need your help and that of your men. We have heard of your reputation as an Apache fighter. You will soon see that these bloodthirsty Indians are the equal of any Apache."

Anza glanced at the Governor sharply. He had been shocked and sorry to hear of the death of Father Jaume but he had also observed the California Indians. Weak, cringing creatures, armed only with a few flimsy arrows and curved rabbit sticks, they scarcely resembled the warlike Apaches. A handful of Spanish soldiers should be able to control them. But he remembered that Rivera was Governor of California and that both men were soldiers of the King.

"I will be glad to assist you," he told Rivera, "but I cannot delay too long. I am under orders from Viceroy Bucareli to take these people north to Monterey, then to select the site for a new settlement on the shores of the Great Bay."

Rivera tossed his head impatiently. "Your people will be just as well off staying here. This is the rainy season and the road to Monterey is much too boggy for travel now. As for the settlement—" He dismissed the subject with a snap of his fingers. "I explored the bay region two years ago and advised the government against a settlement there. It is a damp, miserable place with no proper site for a town. I recommend that you forget the matter."

Anza's dark eyes met those of the Governor. He wondered if he had traveled six hundred miles to make yet another enemy.

Days Of Darkness

ANZA WAS DEEPLY DISTURBED by the way in which Governor Rivera had dismissed his plans for the new settlement on San Francisco Bay, but in all fairness he conceded that the uprising at San Diego was absorbing the man's entire attention. Though it meant a delay in carrying out his own orders, Anza believed that it would take little time to put down a few rebellious, poorly armed savages.

He immediately gave orders for seventeen of his soldiers to prepare to ride to San Diego with him. Lieutenant Moraga would remain behind in charge of the settlers. He also ordered a pack train assembled to carry the equipment required for the short journey and to bring back needed supplies to San Gabriel. Last of all, he summoned Father Font to leave in his keeping the key to the box in which the quadrant was kept.

To his surprise, the priest appeared angry. "Why did you not tell me of your plans to go to San Diego? Why must I always learn of your wishes through your servants?" he demanded.

"I did not think you were interested," Anza replied gruffly.

"Not interested!" Father Font drew himself up stiffly. "I came on this journey for one reason: to ride beside you and be your companion, to give you spiritual help when you needed comfort, conversation when you were lonely, advice when you were in doubt. Yet not once on this entire journey have you ever asked me to share your burdens."

Anza looked at him in astonishment. He thought of those lonely hours by the campfire when he had struggled with decisions that had seemed too big for one man. It had never occurred to him that he might have asked Father Font's advice. A proud, independent man, he had never found it easy to ask help of anyone.

"I am still your servant, merely awaiting your request," Father Font continued.

Even now Anza found it hard to forget his pride. "Well, I have a request then," he muttered. "Come to San Diego with me. I would be grateful for your company."

Instantly Father Font was smiling. "I will be very pleased to ride with you." As the priest hurried away Anza's eyes followed him thoughtfully. Father Font was not an easy man to know, but it was hard for the commander to admit that he himself might have been to blame for many of his own troubled hours.

In spite of good intentions, Anza had little chance to talk with Father Font on the trip to San Diego. Governor Rivera, who rode with them, accompanied by twelve soldiers from the presidio, claimed most of his attention. At night the Governor insisted on a double guard around their camps, so fearful was he of Indian attack. On the second day out they camped near the abandoned site of the San Juan Capistrano mission. Later, when they made camp on the beach, some friendly Indians offered them firewood and fish. Angrily, Governor Rivera drove them away but Father Font bartered secretly for some large sardines which he roasted in the coals and which he and Anza enjoyed for their dinner that night.

Four days later they were welcomed eagerly by the soldiers and refugees at the presidio in San Diego. The log and adobe fort was located on the slope of a hill which overlooked the entrance to a small valley as well as the distant sea. The blackened ruins of the mission lay farther up the valley.

From Father Fuster Anza learned that both Christian and heathen Indians had taken part in the midnight attack. The original plan of the rebellion had called for the mission and presidio to be attacked at the same time. However, when the first party of Indians had set fire to the mission ahead of the signal, the second party, certain that the soldiers would be alerted by the flames, had called off the attack on the fort. Racing back up the valley, they had joined with

their brothers in sacking the mission. Together with
Father Jaume, a blacksmith and a carpenter had also
been murdered. Father Fuster and the four soldiers
had been able to barricade themselves and had fought
off the attackers until daylight when they had retreated
to the presidio. Throughout the night the sentries at
the fort had never once noticed the distant flames of
the burning mission.

It seemed to Anza that the soldier guards at both
mission and fort had neglected their duty. To his surprise, however, Governor Rivera did not blame the
guards but blamed instead the young lieutenant in
charge of the presidio, even though the man had been
absent in San Juan Capistrano at the time. The lieutenant was well liked by the Fathers and Anza sensed
once again the growing conflict between the military
forces and the Church in California. He noted that
the Governor showed great concern over the minor
wounds of the neglectful soldiers and little sorrow for
the death of Father Jaume.

Unlike the San Gabriel Mission, the mission at San
Diego had few cultivated fields. The Indians remained
in their villages, coming for instruction to the mission
but once a week. Now all had fled to their homes.
Anza would have preferred to take a party of soldiers
directly into the villages to challenge the Indians boldly
or to bluff them with a show of strength.

Governor Rivera showed no desire to meet the Indians face to face. Instead, he sent soldiers to bring
back culprits. Because the Indians saw them coming,

the soldiers were able to capture only two men. When the Governor questioned the captives without getting any satisfactory answers, he ordered them whipped and released. The following day the soldiers returned with two more Indians. This time Rivera ordered that the prisoners be given fifty lashes before questioning. As a result, one Indian died and the other was made too ill to talk. Soon this became the pattern of the passing days: soldiers bringing in prisoners, followed by trials, floggings, and other punishments.

Confined to the crowded presidio, Anza grew more and more restless. He had come south expecting to assist in a military campaign. He was of no use to the Governor in these endless trials. As days grew into weeks, it was becoming ever clearer to Anza that Governor Rivera was opposed to the founding of the San Francisco settlement. When Rivera suggested that Anza return to Mexico, leaving the settlers in his charge, Anza began to suspect that he was being held in San Diego simply to delay the carrying out of his orders from Viceroy Bucareli.

Father Font shared his suspicion. "Of course Governor Rivera is trying to delay you," the priest said angrily one day as the two men talked together in the small room they shared at the presidio. "Rivera has explored the bay region and, after seeing a few sand dunes, has reported to the King that the place is not suitable for a settlement. Now you arrive with orders to select a site for both a town and a mission. If you are successful, *you* will get the glory and *he* will look like a fool."

"Perhaps you are right, Father," Anza agreed. "But I am also a soldier. I cannot desert the Governor as long as he believes there is danger of an Indian attack. We will have to wait a little longer. Perhaps something will happen to change his mind."

Anza did not have long to wait. A few days later an urgent message arrived from Lieutenant Moraga. Supplies were growing low at San Gabriel. Father Paterna had been forced to reduce the colonists to half-rations. Grumbling and discontent were mounting daily among the people. Anza hurried with the letter to Rivera. Finally, Rivera gave Anza permission to return to his colonists, but he did so in such a grudging manner that the commander knew he would be leaving a bitter enemy behind him.

Torrential rains held Anza prisoner at San Diego for a few more days, but once on the road his spirits revived. His cheerfulness did not last long, however. At San Gabriel Mission more bad news awaited him. Five men had deserted in the night, stealing part of the supplies and thirty head of horses. Just an hour before Anza's arrival, Lieutenant Moraga and seven soldiers had started after the runaways. But even more alarming than this was the morale of the settlers. On the journey, hardships shared had held them together. Now, after a month of idleness, they had grown quarrelsome and bitter. Where they once had idolized Anza, they now blamed him for short rations, poor pay, and failure to live up to the fine promises he had given them in Mexico.

As though to complete this round of misery, Anza was taken ill. For four days he lay sick while a black and terrible depression swept over him. He had brought his people safely from Mexico only to have them turn against him. With his goal almost in sight, new obstacles had appeared in his way. First had been the delay in San Diego, then the theft of the horses, and now his own illness. He had expected cooperation from the authorities. Instead, Governor Rivera, the most powerful man in California, seemed determined to keep him from carrying out his orders.

His thoughts went back to other times when fate had barred his way—the long years of Indian fighting that had delayed his first expedition, the Apache raids that twice had taken his horses, the dreary months at Terrenate that had kept him from presenting his reports to Viceroy Bucareli. Almost it seemed that he had been born under some star of ill fortune that turned moments of triumph into despair.

Father Font was his constant companion during these days of darkness. The Father tried to engage Anza in conversation and played to him on the psaltery, a small stringed instrument resembling a harp. At first Anza paid little attention, but on the sixth day Father Font succeeded in engaging his attention.

"You are a man of action," the priest began. "This waiting is what is making you ill. If you would take half of the settlers and what supplies and horses we have and start for Monterey, you would soon feel better."

"How can I start north with only some of the people?" Anza answered irritably. "It is four hundred miles to Monterey. I must wait until I learn what has happened to Lieutenant Moraga."

"What is wrong with you that you cannot give responsibility to others?" Father Font demanded. "You chose Lieutenant Moraga and Sergeant Grijalva because they were capable men. Let them carry some of your burdens. Your health is the important thing. Nothing matters at this moment except that you get well."

Remembering the coldness between them in the past, Anza was startled. "You are most kind, but my health hardly seems that important," he murmured.

"You are wrong," Father Font insisted. "Governor Rivera is a cold and stubborn man. He is determined to keep you from going to San Francisco. You are the one man in California strong enough to stand up against him. You must find the strength to go on. If anything happens to you, we also lose all hope for the mission and settlement at San Francisco."

Anza realized that Father Font was giving him good advice. Never before had he let obstacles stand in his way. Once he was on horseback again he would regain his strength. He sat up abruptly. "You are right. I must get back in the saddle. Without waiting for the Lieutenant we will start for Monterey." Accustomed to being the leader, Anza still found it hard to admit he had taken advice from anyone. "In fact, I was about to decide to do this," he concluded.

Father Font gave him a searching look. But for once he was wise enough to make no comment.

Father Font had been right. Two days later, as Anza started north with half of the settlers, his health seemed to return. Once on the trail the colonists gave up their complaining and again accepted him as their trusted leader.

Because it was the rainy season muddy trails slowed the travelers' progress, but now they were following a well-traveled route. Along the way they found good camp sites and friendly Indians. On the eleventh day, as they approached the San Luis Obispo Mission, most of the settlers changed into their best clothes in honor of the occasion. Also, only a short distance from the mission itself they had to cross a great mire and many fell from their horses into the mud. The lonely mission Fathers did not mind the bedraggled appearance of the newcomers, however. They were welcomed into the mission church, mud and all.

Later, at the San Antonio Mission, the same warm welcome awaited the travelers. Here Lieutenant Moraga caught up with the caravan. Leaving Sergeant Grijalva to escort the remaining settlers, he had ridden ahead to report to Anza concerning the runaway thieves. Because they had taken the best horses, he had found it difficult to catch up with them. But he had not given up and had followed them over the mountains, down to San Sebastián, then out into the desert, finally overtaking them just ten miles from the lagoon at Santa Olaya. Not only had Moraga brought back the prisoners and all that was stolen, but on the return trip his men had rounded up a number of the horses and cattle abandoned on the first crossing. Anza had reason to be very proud of his young lieutenant.

Three days later, on March 10, the settlers arrived at Monterey in the pouring rain. The long journey was over. One hundred and thirty days had passed since they had left Tubac. The settlers from Culiacán had ridden two thousand miles. A final welcome was given them at the presidio.

Though Monterey was the capital of California, the presidio was not large. Built around a square, it consisted of barracks, storehouses, a chapel, the commander's house, and a few tule huts. Anza's soldiers shared barracks with the presidio guard while the settlers set up tents in the square; but there were few accommodations for the leaders of the party. That first evening, Anza and Father Font rode over the hill to stay at the Carmel Mission. Here Anza received the welcome that meant most to him. Father Junípero Serra led him to the door of the church. Father Font sprinkled him with holy water. The seven brown-robed priests who escorted him inside began to sing. The first and most difficult part of Anza's mission had been accomplished. He had delivered the first overland settlers to Monterey.

Cross On The Hill

EVER SINCE HIS FIRST visit to Monterey Anza had enjoyed the friendship of the mission Fathers. It was good
to be reunited with them again, particularly Father
Palóu with whom he had shared so many dreams. But
he had not forgotten his conversation with Father
Font at San Gabriel.

The friars, well aware of the Governor's opposition
to the settlement at San Francisco, urged Anza to lose
no time in starting north. "Brothers Palóu, Murguía,
and Peña have been living with us two years waiting
for their promised mission. If they do not get it soon
I may have to send them back to Mexico," Father Serra
told Anza as they were gathered that night around the
dinner table.

Anza nodded, knowing what was in the Father's
mind. Though Anza carried orders from the Viceroy,

Governor Rivera was a powerful man. If the Governor returned unexpectedly from San Diego he still might find a way to block Anza's plans. "Do not worry, Father," he said at last. "I plan to start tomorrow. Since Father Palóu accompanied Governor Rivera on his exploration two years ago, perhaps you would like to send him with me now."

Father Serra shook his head. "I would like to, but I dare not. You have seen how things stand. If I send one of my brothers, it will look to the Governor as if I am choosing sides. Long after you have returned to Mexico we must continue to try to live here in peace."

"I have seen the situation," Anza replied. "This morning I started a letter to the Governor, telling him of my plans and taking full responsibility. My orders require only that I select the site, but in my letter I have volunteered to remain in California, at my own expense, long enough to escort the settlers to San Francisco personally and direct the building of the fort. It is my hope this may ease the situation between you."

"You are very understanding," Father Serra began. His face paled suddenly. "Commander, what is it?"

With a cry Anza had lurched from his chair, clutching his side. Father Peña caught him as he fell. It took the strength of several priests to carry him to his bed.

The presidio surgeon was hastily summoned, but he was unable to ease Anza's searing pain and his mounting fever. From historical accounts, the illness appears to have been an attack of appendicitis for which there was no relief in those days. For almost a week Anza lay ill while the Fathers hovered, white-faced and anxious, around him. In spite of his pain he managed to send off his letter to the Governor. Over and over he kept insisting that he must be up and on his way.

Finally, disgusted with the futile efforts of the surgeon, he asked Father Font to bring him some roots from an herb he had carried all the way from Sonora. With the priest's help he ground these and prepared a burning salve which he applied to his body. To everyone's astonishment his fever abated and the pain began to decrease.

On the sixth day of his illness, in spite of protests from everyone, Anza insisted on being carried to his horse. He rode over the hill to Monterey. The next morning, accompanied by twenty men, including Father Font, Lieutenant Moraga, and several soldiers from the presidio, he started north.

Traveling light, the men reached the great bay within four days. Leaving the others to set up camp at Mountain Lake, near the entrance to the harbor, Anza and Father Font, like excited small boys, set off for a ridge of hills. Moments later they stood on the white cliffs overlooking the Golden Gate.

As a trained military man Anza knew that this site was ideal for a settlement and fort. "Here is where we will build," he cried. "With Spanish cannon trained across the entrance to the harbor, let the Russians come! We shall see how fast they run back again!"

Father Font agreed with the selection of the site. Not only would a small fort be able to control entrance to the vast bay, but near by was a plentiful supply of fresh water from the lake.

The following morning Anza returned to the spot with Lieutenant Moraga and several soldiers and erected a huge wooden cross which could be seen for miles. Under some stones at the base of the cross he placed a document stating that he had been there and had chosen this spot for the location of the new presidio.

The next day the men turned east to explore the shore line of the bay. Here, in a green canyon with rich soil, a sparkling stream, and a waterfall large enough to run a mill, Anza chose the site for the mission. Lieutenant Moraga cleared a small patch of ground and planted some corn and chick-peas. When the Fathers came they would be able to judge what they could expect from the soil. Because it was March 29 and the Friday of Sorrows, Anza named the hill Dolores.

The Spaniards continued south in order to circle the bay. In the distance they saw the "palo alto," or tall tree, which Rivera had noted on his trip. The solitary redwood, visible for many miles, marked the spot where the city of Palo Alto stands today.

In twenty-four hours they reached the tall tree. They stopped briefly while Father Font used his knowledge of trigonometry to calculate its height as one hundred and forty feet.

As they continued on around the bay, heading north now along the western shore line, they saw a few Indians in the distance but most were too frightened to come near even for gifts.

Once, as the men rounded a curve of a hill, they startled a lone Indian coming toward them carrying a huge bundle of grass. At the sight of the first white men and horses he had ever seen, the Indian was so terrified that he threw himself on the ground and made a pitiful effort to hide himself under the grass. Anza ordered the members of his party to stop. Opening a pack, he held out some beads. The men could see the Indian watching them through a tiny peephole in the grass, but he was still too frightened to move. Finally Anza dismounted, gently placed the beads in the Indian's hand, then motioned everyone to ride on.

The only instruction from the Viceroy that remained to be carried out was to determine if the bay was fed by a river. Father Crespi, who had accompanied Fages on his explorations in 1772, insisted he had seen such a river. In San Diego Governor Rivera had insisted just as vehemently that it did not exist. Anza was resolved to keep an open mind but he would not have been human if he had not secretly hoped that his friend, Father Crespi, and not the Governor, would be right.

Continuing north, the party passed Carquinez Strait and stopped near the site of the present town of Antioch. Here, the men tasted the water and found to their amazement that it was fresh.

"Rivera was wrong! This must be the start of the river," Anza cried excitedly.

Father Font would not allow his own dislike of Rivera to cloud his judgment. "No, I do not think it is a river," he replied. "The Governor is right. There is no river. This is a lake." Motioning across the great body of water, he called attention to the fact that there was no current. He pointed out that there were no high watermarks or driftwood such as would have been left by a river during its flood seasons.

Anza was still not convinced. However, when he threw a log into the water it did not float downstream as he had expected but swung gently back to shore. Father Font pointed out more evidence that this was not a river. The water was clear and very deep; it had a slight ebb and flow as though affected by the tides and tiny waves along the shore as a lake would be.

Anza could trust his own judgment in leading a troop of soldiers, selecting a site for a fort, or dealing with Indians, but, coming from the deserts of Sonora, he had had little experience with rivers. The largest he had ever seen was the Colorado, which, even at flood stage, was not much more than six feet deep. It was hard to imagine any river as wide and deep as this body of water. These last weeks he had come to have a grudging admiration for Father Font's scholarly attainments. Had not the Father calculated the height of the great tree? Along the trail was he not able to recognize dozens of varieties of plants and birds and insect life? The priest undoubtedly was right. Anza finally had to agree that they were on the shores of a fresh-water lake.

Still, he wished to be thorough. Ahead of him a vast plain stretched all the way to the distant mountains. He decided that he and his men would press on to the mountains. From the mountain slopes he might obtain a view that would prove Father Font wrong.

They started onto the plain but soon found their way barred by marshes and tules. Realizing that it might take weeks to reach the mountains, Anza gave the order to turn back. By now the colonists would be growing restless at Monterey and the answer to his letter should have arrived from Governor Rivera.

Both Anza and Father Font wrote in their diaries that they had discovered a fresh-water lake, failing to realize that they had actually stood on the delta of the Sacramento, California's great navigable river.

The party returned to Monterey. Father Font at once headed for the mission to pick a friendly argument with Father Crespi about his river. To Anza's dismay, there was no reply to his letter to Governor Rivera.

The Angry Governor

WHILE FATHER FONT visited with his brother friars at Carmel, Anza waited for word from the Governor. He took long walks on the beach with vigorous Father Cambón and made daily inspections of the vegetable garden tended by Father Palóu, but his eyes strayed often to the distant hills, watching for a rider.

On the fourth day after his return, he felt he could delay no longer. "I must return to Mexico," he told Father Serra sadly. "I have carried out all of my orders from Viceroy Bucareli. I have escorted the colonists safely to Monterey and chosen the location for the settlement on San Francisco Bay. Without permission from Governor Rivera I have no right to remain in California and lead the colonists personally to their new home. This task belongs to Lieutenant Moraga who will be their leader at the new presidio."

"It is a sad thing that our Governor is so opposed to the settlement," Father Serra said. "Knowing that you have gone ahead and carried out your orders against his wishes, I fear he purposely does not answer your letter."

Anza nodded. "I have thought of that. I am sending Sergeant Góngora and several soldiers from the presidio with a message inviting the Governor to meet me at San Gabriel on my way south. We are both military men. I still believe that we can sit down together and settle our differences. There is no reason for a quarrel between us. We both take orders from the Viceroy."

Father Serra smiled hopefully. "In that case I will not say farewell. Instead, I will pray for your success with the Governor. Perhaps after all he will grant you permission to escort the colonists to their new home."

For the settlers who had journeyed so far with Anza, it was more difficult to say good-by. Of the two hundred and forty people who had left Tubac, almost two hundred were staying in California. On April 14 everyone gathered in the courtyard of the presidio at Monterey. In the return party were Anza, Father Font, ten escort soldiers, plus an assortment of servants, muleteers, vaqueros, and several travelers going between missions. The pack animals carried supplies for their return trip, along with extra items to be dropped at the missions along the way. Anza himself helped lash a large wooden cage to the back of one mule. Inside were four cats which were being sent to San Gabriel and San Diego where the storerooms were overrun with mice.

It was a sad farewell. The women wept and embraced Anza over and over again. If there had been times along the trail when he had seemed a harsh leader, they were forgotten now. The voices of the men were husky as they wished him a safe journey. Señora Gertrudis held up the baby that had been born on the way. Anza tossed him in the air and gave him a hearty kiss. Then he cleared his throat noisily.

"Vayan Subiendo!" he bellowed. It would not do for these people to see their commander with tears in his eyes.

As the travelers started away from the presidio, many of the younger children followed, shouting and waving until they could no longer keep up.

Lieutenant Moraga rode as far as the first night's camp. Along the way Anza gave him last-minute instructions for taking the settlers on to the site that had been selected. "Do not fear the Governor," Anza told him. "I am the one he distrusts. With me out of the way, you may not find so much opposition."

Lieutenant Moraga smiled. "I am not worried, Colonel. After the snows we faced together on the desert, I do not think the coldness of a Governor will bother me."

Anza laughed. He was going to miss his trusted lieutenant.

The following morning the travelers had barely said good-by to Lieutenant Moraga and started south when they saw horsemen galloping toward them at full speed. One minute the riders appeared on the crest of a hill, the next they dipped from sight behind some trees. There was no mistaking their haste.

As the riders drew closer, Anza recognized Sergeant Góngora and the soldiers whom he had sent with his message to the Governor three days before. The sergeant drew up his horse. "Commander Anza, I bring you letters from the Governor who is traveling north only a few hours behind me."

Anza accepted the packet with a puzzled look. It seemed strange that the Governor should bother to write letters when he was only a short distance away. Glancing toward the others who were gathering curiously, the sergeant reined his horse closer. "Commander, I must speak to you alone!" he whispered.

More puzzled than ever, Anza dismounted. He and the sergeant walked a short distance apart from the others. Here the soldier related in an excited voice the strange events which had taken place since Anza had last seen the Governor.

Once Anza had left San Diego, Rivera had continued his daily procedure of sending out soldiers to bring in Indians for trial and punishment. Among those captured had been one of the ringleaders of the uprising. Somehow this Indian had escaped from the fort's jail and sought refuge in the presidio church. When the friars had refused to turn him over to the soldiers, the Governor had broken into the church and bodily dragged the Indian from in front of the altar. For such a sacrilege Father Fuster had excommunicated the Governor on the spot.

As though this was not enough of a blow, only days later Governor Rivera had received Anza's first letter informing him that he, Anza, was going on to select the site for the presidio at San Francisco against the Governor's wishes. It was believed by the soldiers that these two blows at his authority had temporarily destroyed the man's reason. He had written a reply to Anza, then hastily called back his courier. Several days later, he had told everyone at San Diego that he was going on an Indian campaign. Instead, once out of sight of the presidio, he had ordered his soldiers to head at full speed for Monterey.

Sergeant Góngora and his men had met the Governor on the road not far from San Antonio Mission. Normally, the sergeant was a trusted friend of the Governor. Now, learning that he came from Anza, Rivera had treated him rudely and stripped him of his rank for no apparent reason.

"Commander, I can only believe that my Governor has gone mad!" the sergeant cried. "I had hoped to catch you before you left Monterey. I intend to ask for my discharge and permission to return to Mexico!"

Anza tried to calm the man. He assured him that the Governor must have spoken in anger and that good soldiers were badly needed in California. But when Sergeant Góngora and his men had continued on their way toward Monterey, Anza, greatly troubled, told Father Font what he had learned.

The two men finally decided that the soldier must have exaggerated the situation. There could be only one reason why Rivera was riding north in such haste and that was to confer with Anza. "He probably will expect us to return to Monterey, but we might as well ride on and meet him along the way," Anza said.

They did not have long to wait. They had gone only a few miles when they saw the Governor's party approaching. When it drew close, Anza could scarcely believe his eyes. Governor Rivera was riding a mule. Though it was a warm spring day, he was so swathed in serapes that only a portion of his beard and one of his piercing dark eyes could be seen through the wrappings.

Anza saluted. "Greetings, your Excellency. I trust you are in good health."

"I am ill!" the Governor muttered without meeting Anza's eyes. Calling to a servant, he instructed him to give Anza some mail they were carrying. The man obeyed, explaining that one of the letters was from Father Garcés who was at San Gabriel. Anza was not surprised that the wandering friar's explorations had brought him to California. He wanted to ask more about his old friend but he must first talk with Rivera. "We have much to discuss, sir—" he began.

For the first time Governor Rivera's fiery glance met his. "Good-by!" he roared. Whirling about, he rode on.

Anza stared after him, open-mouthed. A choking anger filled his chest. When the Governor and his party had disappeared over the hills, he called on the others to bear witness and to give him written statements of the occurrence which he could carry back to Mexico. Father Font and another priest traveling to San Antonio de Padua Mission were equally startled by the Governor's rudeness. The following day when they reached the mission both wrote statements for Anza to carry to the Viceroy, telling of the incident.

Anza's party moved on to the mission at San Luis Obispo. That same day the bells rang out to signal another arrival. Hurrying to the courtyard, Anza was startled to see Father Cambón from Carmel.

By now Governor Rivera had arrived in Monterey and had talked to Father Serra. Alarmed by the Governor's behavior, Father Serra had written immediately to the authorities in Mexico. Afraid to trust any of the soldiers for fear the letters might fall into the Governor's hands, he had sent them to Anza by Father Cambón, knowing that Anza would deliver them safely. If Anza was considered a hard-riding commander, Father Cambón was quite a horseman too. He had covered a hundred and fifty miles in less than three days.

Father Cambón also brought a curt note from Governor Rivera, excusing his behavior along the road on the grounds that he was ill and stating that he would like to talk with Anza after all. Anza decided to wait for him at the mission. On the second day a soldier brought a message that the Governor had arrived and was camped in the hills as he was too tired to ride on to the mission. But neither Anza nor Father

Font were fooled by this pretext.

"He still is angry," Father Font said. "This is a flimsy excuse. He has no intention of coming to the mission as long as you are here."

To Anza this was but another in a long line of Rivera's insults. "Perhaps it is just as well," he muttered. Sitting down at a table, he wrote a reply to the Governor, stating that he would be willing to meet him at San Luis Obispo, San Gabriel or wherever Rivera wished, but from now on all communications between them must be in writing.

Anza's letter enraged Rivera but he finally set off for San Gabriel to meet the commander. Anza followed with his men. For the next six days the parties traveled only a short distance apart, but Governor Rivera gave no sign that he knew Anza was behind him. The days in the saddle cooled Anza's temper. He even began to see the humor of the situation. He gave the Governor plenty of time to arrive at San Gabriel first, then sent a friendly note announcing his approach. When he arrived and saw the soldiers lined up to give him the usual salute, Anza concluded that his gesture of friendship had succeeded. But there was no sign of the Governor. He had locked himself in his room and refused to come out while Anza was there.

To avoid an open conflict which might cause a scandal among the troops, Anza set up his tent a short distance from the mission and decided to conduct his remaining business with Rivera by written note. Father Font agreed with him that this was the wisest course.

That night the two men had a serious talk.

"Remember when we stayed here before, how you told me that the founding of the settlement on San Francisco Bay was the most important goal in California?" Anza asked.

Father Font nodded. "Yes. The great bay must be secured for Spain at all costs."

Anza paused before he spoke again. "It is for this reason that I have informed Rivera that I am returning to Mexico in three days."

"I am afraid I do not understand," Father Font replied.

"When we arrived, the Governor's opposition was directed against the founding of the settlement. Now most of it is directed against me. This quarrel between us is foolish. For some reason Rivera sees me as a threat to his authority. He resents my friendship with the mission Fathers. Instead of helping Father Serra, my presence is making things more difficult for him. Though the Governor is temporarily upset, he is a soldier with a long and faithful record of service to the Crown. Lieutenant Moraga is a young man with spirit and determination. If I am gone, I believe the two of them will get together and the settlement will be founded. If I remain, the Governor's pride will make him keep on fighting the settlement just to keep on fighting me."

Anza did not tell Father Font all that was in his heart—how much he had hoped actually to take part in the founding of the new port; how hard it was to turn over such a responsibility to a younger man. But Father Font had a way of guessing what was in his mind. "You are not only a courageous man, Colonel Anza, but a very wise one," he said. "Yes, I think we are both overdue in Mexico."

"All right. Then we start in three days," Anza said gruffly. "And don't try to tell me I will feel better when I am in the saddle again. I know this already!"

Both men chuckled. After the troubles they had shared in California it was hard to recall that only a few months before they scarcely had been friends.

Pablo, The Hero

ON MAY 2, 1776, Anza left San Gabriel to return to Mexico. His party included thirty people and eighty-six horses and mules. Twenty pack animals carried only the lightest supplies for the journey. Most of the load consisted of bear and beaver skins, rare shells, Indian baskets, and other souvenirs he was taking home as gifts for the Viceroy.

Riding with the party was a ten-year-old Indian boy, Pedro, from San Luis Obispo. He was the son of an Indian chief who had been killed in battle. His mother had remarried a Spanish soldier. A lively youngster who spoke excellent Spanish, Pedro was being taken to Mexico City so that Viceroy Bucareli could see a Christianized Indian.

Neither Anza nor Father Font were surprised when Governor Rivera did not appear to see them off. Nor were they surprised when he failed to send any letters for the Viceroy. There was little question that his reports concerning Anza would be unfavorable. No doubt he would send them to Mexico by ship. Anza was not worried. A friend of the Viceroy, soon he would be able to present his version in person. He forwarded a brief note to Lieutenant Moraga telling him what to do if it should eventually prove true that the Governor had lost his reason, thus making it necessary for the young lieutenant to take over military control of California.

Once on his way, Anza's good spirits returned. He forgot his unpleasant encounters with Rivera. Other people filled his thoughts now. Before long he would be seeing his beloved wife, Doña Ana, and his daughters. At the Colorado River he would be meeting his good friends, Chief Palma, Father Eixarch, and Father Garcés.

Because his party was small and traveling light, Anza made good time crossing the mountains. Once over the pass, the travelers saw the desert below them, white and shimmering under the scorching May sun. Because of the heat they made most of the crossing by night. Even so, the animals were close to exhaustion when they reached the lagoon of Santa Olaya ten days after leaving San Gabriel. Unaware that Anza was coming, Chief Palma was not there to greet him, but the Indians camped around the lake presented the Spaniards with squashes and corn and sent messengers to Palma to tell him of Anza's arrival.

Once Anza had rested the animals and set forth again up the Colorado River, most of the encamped Indians accompanied him. At small villages along the way more Indians joined the party, shouting and tossing dirt in their joy at seeing the Spaniards. By the time Anza reached Palma's village he was accompanied by a small army of Indians. Father Eixarch, sun-bronzed and hearty, rushed from his hut. Close beside him was the towering figure of Palma, his child-like face wreathed in smiles. When both men had embraced Anza and Father Font, Palma punched proudly at Father Eixarch's muscular arms and strong back to show Anza in what good health he had kept his friend.

Again, Anza was disappointed to find that he had missed Father Garcés, but from the Indians Father Eixarch had learned that he was visiting a tribe to the east and was safe. Anza immediately sent a messenger to tell the friar that he would wait for him at the Colorado three days. If Father Garcés had not returned in that time, Anza's party would start for Sonora, leaving him to make his own way home.

With Father Garcés away most of the time, it had been a lonely five months for young Father Eixarch, but he had not been idle. When rising waters had threatened his cabin, he had built a new one on higher ground. He had planted a vegetable garden of beans, peas, onions, cauliflower, and other vegetables. When it was possible to do so, he had said Mass for the Indians who cared to attend. He had also instructed them in the ways of Christianity. When visitors came from neighboring tribes, he had presented them with small gifts and had talked to them about living in harmony. On those rare occasions when Father Garcés had returned for a few days, he had diligently copied the older friar's diaries for him in his neat, clear handwriting. Anza could see that Father Garcés had chosen his young assistant wisely.

Father Eixarch's only complaint during the lonely vigil was that he had run short of the wine and candles needed to conduct Mass. When Indians, sent to Caborca on the frontier, failed to return with enough of the needed items, Father Eixarch himself had made a trip back to Mexico to get them, taking Palma's brother Pablo with him as a guide. Along the way, Pablo's horse had given out. Determined not to lose any time, the young friar had ridden on, with the ugly chieftain running beside him on foot most of the way.

Such a remarkable feat should have endeared Pablo to the friar. It had not. Back at the Colorado, Pablo had continued to be a nuisance, boasting, stirring up trouble, and refusing to attend Mass. "He delights in showing off his physical strength but in his heart he has little love for the Spaniards or God," Father Eixarch told Anza.

On the other hand, the young friar had nothing but praise for Chief Palma, who had barely left his side for five months and had attended Mass faithfully.

"Palma tries to set a good example for his people.

His heart is set on the trip to Mexico he will make with you."

Anza frowned. He remembered Palma's disappointment over the fact that the California colonists had not come to live among the Yumas and how, in order to ease the situation, he had told Palma he would take him to Mexico City to see the Viceroy. Anza was a man of his word, but in the intervening months he had hoped that Palma would forget the invitation.

But Palma had not forgotten. That night he came to Anza's tent to discuss the matter. With him were several elders of the tribe. Anza called in Fathers Font and Eixarch to join the discussion. Anza must make the right decision. The Spaniards were well aware that the future of the overland trail to Mexico depended on keeping the friendship of the Yumas who controlled the Colorado crossing. Palma was the undisputed chief, but there was always the chance some lesser chief might use his absence to seize control.

"You may be gone from your people a very long time," Anza told him.

"How long?" Palma wanted to know.

"It might be a year," Anza replied.

"I do not care if it is two years. I wish to go with my brother to see his great leader," Palma insisted.

"What about your people? Who will rule them while you are gone?" Anza asked.

Palma then explained that he had appointed two elders of the tribe to rule in his absence. By wisely choosing two men, Palma had insured that neither would seize control.

Anza then insisted that Palma take other Indians with him as traveling companions. Thus, if some unforeseen misfortune overtook the chief while he was in Mexico, Anza could be sure there would be Indian witnesses to the fact that the Spaniards had treated him fairly. Palma first chose one of his brothers. Anza then suggested that Palma also include his nephew, Pablo's son. He made the invitation sound like a great honor. The secret smiles that passed between Father Font and Father Eixarch told him that they saw through his strategy. Anza still did not trust Pablo. With his son a hostage in the hands of the Spaniards, there was little chance that the ugly chieftain would cause any trouble.

It was midnight when the meeting broke up, but Anza was convinced he had made every arrangement to keep the Yuma Crossing open.

Father Eixarch had come to like the Yumas so well that he wished to remain with them. Anza explained that he could not allow this as he had orders to take him back to Mexico. The next morning the friar packed his few belongings, abandoned his carefully tended little vegetable garden, and joined Anza on the bank of the river. The river was flooded now with the spring runoff and Anza planned to use the time while waiting for Father Garcés to make the difficult crossing.

In places the river was a half-mile wide, churning with red-brown mud and speckled with debris and bobbing trees washed down from upstream. Anza ordered the horses driven to a place where the river was extremely wide but where there was little current. However, for the crossing of men and supplies, he chose the narrows where the current was swift but the distance much shorter.

Hoping to delay the Spaniards' departure, on his last visit Palma had protested that his Indians could not swim in rough water. But now that he was going to Mexico with his beloved friend he piped a different tune. The chief ordered his people to cut trees and start building rafts. That day two loads of men and baggage were taken across with difficulty. After the second trip one raft had to be taken apart and pushed back piece by piece because of the swing of the current.

The next day the river was higher than before, but the raft was rebuilt and a few more men made it safely across. Again the raft was taken apart in order to get it back to the opposite shore. Aware that this way the crossing was going to take forever, Anza ordered the smaller items given to the Indian women to transport. These were put into woven baskets, which the women pushed ahead of them as they swam to the opposite shore.

That afternoon, when the raft had been reassembled, Anza, the two Fathers, and eleven others prepared to cross. They had barely pushed away from shore when one end of the raft began to sink. Two of the soldiers leaped for the bank and were hauled to safety by the Indians as the raft with the others aboard was swept out into the stream and into a whirlpool. The raft began to sink still further. The Indians on the bank called to the men to jump.

Pablo, who had been swimming beside the raft in order to steer it, had somehow managed to retain his hold.

Suddenly he began to shout. "Cowards! Cowards!" he cried. "Stay on the shore. I, Pablo, will get them across if I have to carry each man by myself!"

His taunts encouraged the swimmers to seize the raft again and start pushing it forward. As they struggled, the whole raft became awash with water. Whooping and shouting, the Indians on the bank leaped into the river and swam to join the others, seizing the raft wherever they could find a hold.

Splashing, grunting, and straining, they kept the craft moving. By the time they reached the middle of the river, it was well under water. One of the soldiers aboard, getting into the spirit of the thing, fired his musket. This was something the Indians loved. They shouted and screamed and swam harder. In only twelve minutes they had the raft safely across, though by now it was so far under water that the Spaniards were wet to their knees.

Pablo, for all his many faults, had been proved a hero. He was not a graceful one. That night at the campfire his boasting was almost more than anyone could bear.

The following day the remaining men and baggage were brought across the river.

The three days Anza had promised to wait for Father Garcés were up. The party must be on its way. Anza knew that the friar, accustomed to wandering, would safely make his own way home. Anza decided not to follow the long, winding route up the Gila River, back to Tubac. Instead, he took the Devil's Highway, the shortcut to the capital. This was the route he had followed on his first expedition.

For two days many of the Yumas continued to follow the travelers, reluctant to part with their chief. But when the way led south into the desert country, Palma persuaded them to return home. Though summer was approaching, the soldiers now knew where the water holes were. The company made the desert crossing without trouble. At Caborca Father Eixarch left the group to return to his own mission. On June 1, fifteen days after they had left the Colorado River, the travelers reached Horcasitas, the capital of Sonora.

Doña Ana had come from Tubac to greet her husband. Governor Crespo had prepared a hero's welcome for Anza. Since leaving Horcasitas, the commander had traveled three thousand miles. The night of his arrival the entire town turned out for a fandango in the town square. Anza played host. Standing beside him in his fancy dress uniform was Chief Palma as guest of honor.

My Indian Brother

SHORTLY AFTER THEY reached Sonora, Father Font followed Father Eixarch's example and returned to his home mission, but business and military affairs kept Anza in Horcasitas until August. When he finally started south to Mexico City with Palma, there no longer was any need to hurry. He traveled slowly enough so that his Indian friends could see the sights of Mexico along the way. Palma was particularly impressed by Mexico's beautiful churches. "Someday a church like one of these will stand on the Colorado," he told the Spaniard.

It was October when they reached Mexico City. On the evening of October 26, 1776, Anza knelt before Viceroy Bucareli and presented his reports on the expedition. Scarcely waiting to receive the Viceroy's congratulations, Anza told him of Palma's visit to the capital and the chief's hope for a settlement and mission among the Yumas. Viceroy Bucareli agreed with Anza that the friendship of the Yumas must be kept, but for the moment he was more excited about Palma's arrival in the capital. "You mean the great Yuma chieftain has come all the way to Mexico just to see me?" he exclaimed. "I must talk to him at once."

"Your Excellency, Palma is a simple savage. I have not had time yet to instruct him for an appearance in Spanish society," Anza replied.

"Who cares about society? Others will have a chance to meet him later," Bucareli retorted. "For his first visit I will grant him a private audience so he will not feel ill at ease."

Anza was determined that Palma should make a good impression. He arranged for the chief to wear the uniform the Viceroy had given him and had his two Indian traveling companions outfitted in the long cloaks worn by the men on the Sonoran border. Remembering the enthusiastic bear hugs with which Palma always greeted Spanish arrivals at the Yuma Crossing, Anza carefully explained that one did not greet a viceroy in this way. Palma was a good pupil. At the audience he conducted himself with the dignity and grace of visiting royalty. Anza could see that Viceroy Bucareli was much impressed.

At the Viceroy's suggestion, Anza helped Palma prepare a petition to the Spanish Government. The document was six pages long. In it Palma gave his life history as chief of the Yumas and told of his love for the

Spaniards and his desire to live under their God and their rule. He asked for Christian baptism for himself and his companions and the establishment of a mission among his people. At Palma's request, Anza put his own signature at the bottom of the petition. Above it Palma and his two companions signed with three crosses.

Viceroy Bucareli was in favor of establishing a mission at the Yuma Crossing, but such an undertaking could not be arranged overnight. Bucareli was pressed by other problems. He was still awaiting final word concerning the establishment of the presidio and mission at San Francisco. Also, there had been fresh Indian uprisings along the border, particularly in the region of Mexico. Besides, with presidios and missions spread thin along a dozen other fronts, the question of a new mission would have to be weighed and considered at length.

Fortunately, the Viceroy could take immediate action on Palma's plea for baptism. The chief and his companions were assigned to Father Juan Campa for instruction in the catechism. Father Eixarch had laid the groundwork for this instruction. Father Campa soon reported that the Yumas were making progress in spite of the language barrier.

While the Yumas studied, Anza tried to enjoy the social life of the capital, but he soon found it boring. His thoughts turned worriedly to Lieutenant Moraga and Father Garcés. Fortunately for his peace of mind, word soon reached Mexico City that both had completed their missions successfully.

Anza learned that Lieutenant Moraga had indeed encountered difficulty with Governor Rivera. However, as Anza had suspected, once he himself had left the country, the two men managed a partial truce. In June, as Anza was reaching Sonora, the Lieutenant had been making plans to move the settlers north to their new home. Before they could set out, the supply ship, the *San Carlos,* had arrived. She not only carried supplies for Monterey but for the new settlement at San Francisco as well. In addition, her captain had orders to pick up two Spanish cannon to be carried north to guard the harbor entrance, and to go ashore with his crew to assist the colonists in building their houses and the fort. Faced with this new evidence of the Viceroy's determination to go ahead with the settlement, most of the Governor's resistance crumbled.

Unfortunately, the little *San Carlos* had been blown far off her course by a severe storm. By the time she fought her way back to San Francisco, the settlers already were well established. But the sailors were greeted joyfully and had pitched in with what work remained. On September 17, 1776, the official ceremonies marking the founding of the presidio had been observed. On October 8, Father Palóu presided over the dedication of the mission. Both events had been celebrated with a barbecue and there were many in the crowd who remembered Anza with affection.

As the weeks in Mexico City lengthened, Anza grew more and more restless. The Viceroy had not told him what was to be his next assignment. He knew that there was little chance he would return to Tubac. In his absence the main garrison had been transferred north to Tucson and the small settlement was rapidly falling into ruin under Apache raids. Anza was hopeful that he might be put in charge of the founding of the new settlement at the Yuma Crossing. He felt that he would be the logical choice to command the new presidio if it became a reality. After years of Indian fighting it would be a joy to live among Indians who were friends. He himself had seen the rich river lands where the Indians grew squash and maize and watermelons. Under Spanish ploughs these lands could send a steady flow of needed produce into both California and Sonora. Whenever he had a chance, Anza spoke of these matters to Viceroy Bucareli. Always the Viceroy agreed with him but always he was harassed and overworked with other problems.

In November Palma and the other Indian guests were presented to Mexico City society at a special reception in honor of the King's birthday. The Viceroy himself ordered suitable clothes tailored for them. Palma was a striking figure in a shiny blue uniform with gold buttons and scarlet vest trimmed in gold braid. His brother and nephew wore uniforms only slightly less elegant. The three stalwart Indians created quite a stir at the court function. They remained poised and dignified throughout the ceremonies. Only Anza suspected that they were almost overwhelmed by the pageantry.

On February 13, 1777, Father Campa reported that
the chief and his friends were ready for baptism. The
ceremonies were held in the great cathedral, the finest
church in the New World. A canon of the Church
officiated and almost everyone of importance in Mexico
City attended. With Anza as his godfather, Palma was
baptized Salvador Carlos Antonio. Salvador was the
name Anza and the other Spaniards had given him
when they first met him at the river. The name Carlos
was in honor of the King, Antonio was for the Viceroy.
Palma's companions were baptized at the same time.

Shortly after this, Anza started back to Sonora with
his Indian friends. Along the way Palma talked continually of the promised Spanish settlement and mission
among his people. However, Anza knew that changes
taking place in the city they had left behind them might
well make impossible the chief's dream.

The previous year José de Gálvez had been appointed
new Minister General of the Indies and head of all the
Spanish colonies in the Americas. Gálvez had ordered
many reforms. One of these was to take the frontier
provinces of Sonora, Texas, New Mexico, and California out of the hands of the overworked Bucareli and
place them under a separate Commander General, Teo-
doro de Croix. The purpose of this move was to relieve
Viceroy Bucareli of some of his burdens as well as to
provide more active leadership in the struggle against
the Indians on the border.

These affairs and their possible effect on his own
career were much in Anza's mind as the return journey

progressed. It was not long before a courier from Mexico City caught up with the party and delivered the commander's new orders. He had been appointed Governor of New Mexico! Croix had heard of Anza's abilities as an Indian fighter and he also knew of the King's wish to reward him for his latest service to the Crown.

Anza could not help but be flattered by this honor, especially when he had been expecting only the command of a frontier presidio. Yet he was disappointed too, for it meant giving up his dreams and returning to his old job of Indian fighting. Almost as though his disappointment had been anticipated, a postscript had been added to his orders. Once the Indian troubles had been taken care of in New Mexico, Anza would have permission to lead a new expedition to open the trail from Santa Fé to California.

Palma tried to share his friend's joy at this honor, but, when it was time for them to part, it was hard for the chief to conceal his disappointment that Anza would not be returning with him to the Yuma Crossing.

"Your Viceroy has promised that soon he will send other Spaniards to live among my people," he said, "but it is you, my brother, that I will miss with all my heart."

"We will see each other again when I bring the expedition from New Mexico," Anza assured him.

Palma's eyes filled with tears. "I will wait for you, my brother. If it takes many, many years, I will wait beside our river."

Most of his life Anza had bitterly hated all Indians. Yet, from the first day they had met, he had felt a strange friendship for this tall chief who was now his godson. He too was saddened by the parting. As he watched Palma ride away he did not know the tragedy that lay ahead—that he would never see Palma again or that, from his lonely outpost beside the Colorado, the one Indian whom he had trusted would reach back to ruin his life.

Martyrs To The Dream

ALWAYS ONE TO SET his eyes on far horizons, Anza looked forward to the day when he would lead his third expedition from Santa Fé to California. But first there was work to be accomplished in New Mexico. So that there would be no misunderstanding, Croix listed Anza's orders. He was to find a more direct route between Santa Fé and Sonora; break up an existing alliance between the Navajos and Apaches; make a treaty with the Comanches; save the Hopis, who were threatened with starvation; and strengthen the isolated settlements of the province.

It was a task that might have overwhelmed a man of lesser stature. Anza accepted the orders as though they were no more than he had expected. However, before he could undertake his new duties, there were still further orders from Croix. There had been a Seri uprising in Sonora. Anza was instructed to put down this insurrection and make sure that all was well in Sonora before he assumed his new post.

For almost a year Anza was busy fighting the Seris. It was the spring of 1778 before all seemed quiet on the Sonoran frontier, and Anza, with Doña Ana, headed east to Chihuahua. Here he conferred with Commander General Croix, then moved on to Santa Fé, arriving there late that year.

For both Anza and his wife there was a certain pride in being the "first family" of the small capital, but Anza soon left social duties to Doña Ana while he launched into the tasks assigned him. The Comanches claimed his first attention. His orders had been to form an alliance with them, but on his arrival he found they were on the warpath. Anza led two successful campaigns against the Comanches. Their great leader was Chief Cuerno Verde, or "green horn," named for the green-painted buffalo horns he wore on his headdress. Anza pursued Cuerno Verde as far north as the present state of Colorado, where he trapped the chief in a canyon and killed him and every member of his war party. As a result of this defeat, the Comanches formed an alliance with the Spaniards that lasted a full generation. They joined Anza in fighting the Apaches, their mutual enemy.

Next, Anza turned his attention to the Hopis. These were the Indians who had treated Father Garcés so badly. Though they traded with the Spanish and led no war parties against them, they refused Christianity, saying the white man should keep his God and they would keep theirs. Now, due to several years of drought, they were starving. Apaches and Utes took advantage of their weakness by constantly attacking them.

Anza sent a party to try to persuade the Hopis to move south to new pueblos along the Rio Grande where they would find fertile fields for their crops. Here, inadvertently, Anza's good friend Father Garcés was to help him once again. A few of the Hopis, remembering the friar's visit and his strange banner, blamed their present plight on the friar's vengeance. Had not that forbidding banner shown a burning human? Now their lands were burning. Thus a few Hopis were persuaded to return south with the Spanish soldiers, but the majority chose to remain in their pueblos even if it meant starvation. Anza himself led a party to take the Hopis pack loads of grain. The Hopis were a proud people. In five years their population had dropped from seven thousand to seven hundred. Anza persuaded only a few to move south, but the grain he brought was enough to save the others until they were able to harvest crops again.

Next, Anza led a party which successfully opened a shorter route to Sonora. The fortification of the New Mexico settlements was a more difficult problem. Unlike the people of Sonora who chose to live in well-fortified presidios, the settlers of New Mexico lived on scattered ranchos. Their settlements often consisted of individual ranches strung out for a mile or more along a friendly river bottom. Anza was able to persuade some of the people to move closer together in walled villages, but others resisted his efforts in spite of frequent Indian attacks.

Busy as he was in his new duties, Anza thought often of Palma, Father Garcés, and his other friends in Sonora and California. By means of the slow-traveling mail and news that reached New Mexico, he was able to keep up to some extent with what was happening to them. By now his old enemy, Rivera, had been replaced by a new governor, Felipe de Neve, in California. In 1779 all Mexico had been saddened by the death of Viceroy Bucareli. Though the frontier provinces and California were no longer under his control, Bucareli had repeatedly urged Commander General Croix to hasten with the settlement at the Yuma Crossing.

Croix was a hard-working administrator but a man of limited vision. From the beginning he had little interest in either Sonora or California. To him, the Indian troubles on the eastern frontier seemed more important. With Bucareli still in charge of the supply ships, and men like Father Serra, Governor Neve, and Lieutenant Moraga as leaders, California managed by itself. Anza had left Sonora in good order. Only the matter of the Yuma settlements suffered from Croix's neglect. Finally, in 1779, Father Garcés and Father Díaz were at last sent to build the first mission. A year later they were followed by a handful of colonists and two more friars who founded two small settlements on the Colorado.

Anza was relieved to hear this news. Palma had waited for the missions a long time. When his own work in New Mexico was finished and he led his next overland expedition to California, he looked forward to finding Spaniards living at the Yuma Crossing.

Because of the distances involved, it took months for news to travel from one frontier to another. It was late in 1781 when a party of soldiers galloped into Santa Fé with the latest dispatches from Mexico City and mail from the other provinces. "Commander, I bring terrible news!" a white-faced sergeant cried as he slid from his horse. "You will find it here in your mail, but everywhere along the way it is the talk of the settlements!"

"Speak up, man! Tell me quickly!" Anza said, ushering the courier into his office.

"The Yumas have risen against the Spanish!" the soldier cried. "Former Governor Rivera and thirty Spanish soldiers, Father Garcés and three other friars, have been murdered at the Yuma Crossing by Palma! Spanish women and children have been taken into slavery!"

Anza's face blanched. He staggered as though someone had struck him. "Not Palma, my godson! No, this cannot be true!"

But when Anza read the reports sent by Croix and others he found the terrible news was all too true. Ignoring the advice of Bucareli, Anza, and all who had visited the Yumas, Croix had waited too long in filling Palma's request. From birth, Palma had been no more than just one of many chiefs among the Yumas. It had been his courage, as well as the special attention shown him by the Spaniards, that had boosted him to his position of leadership. After his return from Mexico, when his Spanish friends failed to arrive with the promised missions, he began to fall into disfavor with his people. Twice he made the trip back to Altar to plead personally for the promised missions.

Finally, Croix sent Father Garcés and Father Díaz with a few soldiers, but they came too late. Furthermore, in line with a new drive for economy, Croix refused to send gifts to the Indians. To the disappointed Yumas, these new Spaniards were not at all like Commander Anza with his friendly laughter, his praise and bright trinkets for everyone. That winter Father Díaz returned to Mexico to plead for help. The next year twenty-one soldier-colonists arrived with their families and founded two small settlements on the river. From the beginning they were doomed to failure. Once again, no gifts had been included for the Indians. The settlements were neither presidios nor missions and the friars had little control over the soldiers. Where Anza had sung and danced around the Yuma campfires in friendship, these new Spaniards showed few signs of friendliness. They scorned the Indians, seized their best lands, and let their cattle destroy the Indians' crops.

Finally, even Palma joined Pablo and the other rebel chiefs in believing his white friends had betrayed him. To the Yumas, the final outrage came in June, 1781, when the arrogant Rivera came through the crossing with an escort of a dozen soldiers and forty colonists bound for California. The soldiers mistreated the Indians, laughed when their cattle trampled the Yumas' crops, and failed to pay the Indians for help at the crossing. Perhaps because of some last plea from Palma, the settlers were allowed to move on safely toward California. Rivera and his soldiers remained beside the river to rest their mounts.

On July 17 the Yumas attacked the settlements, killing the friars and the other men and taking the women and children prisoners. The following day, July 18, they swam the river and killed Rivera and all his soldiers. The massacre was one of the worst in Spanish colonial history. Except for an occasional armed patrol, it meant that the Yuma route to California was closed forever to the Spaniards. It would not be opened again until the arrival of the American fur trappers.

Of course Anza's dispatch from Croix did not include an account of these circumstances which led to the massacre. They remained to be recorded later by historians. It contained only the brief, terrible news of the disaster and a certain sharp, cold tone that should have been a warning. Anza was too crushed by the news to take heed of the new and distinctly unfriendly note in the letter. He thought of Father Garcés, the beloved friar who had been his long-time friend. He thought of young Father Díaz who also had accompanied him on that first expedition. Most of all he thought of Palma, his own godson, who had promised to wait for him beside their river.

While Anza was recovering from the stunning effect of this tragic news, forces were already at work in retaliation for this shocking blow to Spanish pride. Fages, explorer and former Governor of California, led two expeditions to the Colorado to ransom the prisoners and recover the bodies of the friars.

But this was not enough. The government demanded that someone be held accountable for the disaster. Fearful for his own career, Croix must have realized that he was the most likely candidate because of his failure to heed Bucareli's repeated warnings. He immediately took steps to place the blame upon both Anza and Father Garcés. He pointed out that the two men were the ones who had made friends with the Yumas in the first place and had led everyone to believe they were friendly to the Spaniards. Father Garcés was dead and could not defend himself. Anza, far away on the New Mexico border, could not defend himself either. Even Bucareli, Anza's protector, was gone.

In 1783 Croix called a meeting of high-ranking frontier officials to discuss the matter. Anza was not invited. Governor Neve of California joined Croix in holding Anza solely responsible for the Yuma massacre.

Rumors of these events must have reached Anza in New Mexico. But he was a soldier first. Putting aside his own feelings, he continued with the work assigned him. He completed his assignment of successfully winning the Navajos away from the Apaches. In 1785 New Mexicans joined Pueblo and Navajo Indians in a campaign that drove the Apaches so far south that for almost ten years New Mexican settlements were free from their attacks. As a final measure, and one he had not been asked to take, Anza made allies of the Utes.

Late in 1783 Croix was promoted to the post of Viceroy of Peru, Neve replacing him as Commander General. Neve had made a fine record in California, but now he was old and disillusioned. Perhaps he feared Anza's power as Rivera had done. Perhaps he merely wanted to avenge the death of the former Governor. He continued the persecution of Anza even more vigorously than Croix.

It was customary in those days for soldiers to draw up a yearly service report, listing their honors. Anza received word that he could no longer list himself as discoverer of the overland route to California. From now on this honor would be accorded to the Indian, Tarabal. In another dispatch he was informed that he could no longer claim to be the conqueror of Cuerno Verde. This honor would be given to a soldier under him.

A third note from Neve brought the final blow. Anza was dismissed as Governor of New Mexico. To add to his humiliation, because for two years a successor was not sent to replace him, he was forced to serve as Governor without benefit of title.

Anza was fifty-three now, his hair gray, old before his time from the hard life he had led. Some said that though he continued to serve with dignity, the news of the Yuma Massacre had divested him of much of his proud spirit. He wrote almost humbly to the Government, asking to be given some minor command in an interior province where he could pass his declining years in relative quiet. The request was ignored.

At last Jacobo de Ugarte, one of Anza's staunch friends, replaced Neve as Commander General. He rallied many of Anza's friends to the old warrior's defense. They petitioned the Minister of the Indies, asking that Anza be given the governorship of Texas. This request also was ignored.

At last, in 1788, Anza's relief arrived in New Mexico. With only a small escort, Anza started south for Mexico City to plead his case in person. On December 19, 1788, he rode into the settlement of Arizpe, some hundred miles below the present Arizona-Mexico border. As he reined up in the plaza before the church, he suddenly clasped his hands to his chest.

"Commander, what is it?" one of the alarmed soldiers cried, springing to his side.

There was no answer. By the time the soldiers had gently lowered him from his horse Anza was dead.

The following day, Juan Bautista de Anza was buried in the church at Arizpe.

If Father Garcés had died a martyr at the hands of the Indians whom he called his people, Anza almost as surely was martyred by his countrymen. But the dreams the two men had shared so long ago in Anza's quarters in Tubac had become a reality. In time, Americans would reopen the Yuma Crossing and build a city on the very spot where Father Garcés' mission had stood. San Francisco would prosper as a lasting monument to

Anza's overland expeditions. Time and history would restore the hard-riding captain to his rightful position as one of New Spain's foremost Indian pacifiers, governors, explorers, and colonizers.

So thoroughly did Anza's enemies erase his name from early records that, following his dismissal as Governor of New Mexico, he seemed to have disappeared completely. For years there was even some conflict among researchers and historians as to whether he had died at Arizpe on his way to the capital, or at Tucson where he had been demoted to captain again. In 1962, in the course of some excavations, the body of Juan Bautista de Anza was discovered under the wooden floor of the Church of Nuestra Señora de la Asuncion at Arizpe. Today his skeleton, clad in full military uniform and encased in a glass-topped coffin, can be seen by all who visit the small four-hundred-year-old church.

Chronology

1735		Juan Bautista de Anza born at Fronteras, Sonora, Mexico.
1753		Enlists in the army following the family tradition.
1755		Promoted to captain.
		Sends petition asking to lead an exploration party overland to California. Petition refused due to Indian uprisings.
1760		Placed in command of his own presidio at Tubac.
1772	May	With Father Garcés, sends a second petition asking to lead an expedition to California.
1773		Petition granted.
1774	January	With Father Garcés, starts out from Tubac with the expedition.
	March	Reaches San Gabriel Mission.
	April	Reaches California capital at Monterey.
	May	Returns to Tubac.
	October	Promoted to lieutenant-colonel.
1775	September	Heads second expedition to California.
1776	January	Arrives safely at San Gabriel Mission. Goes to San Diego to help put down Indian uprisings.
	March	Reaches Monterey with first division of settlers.

		Selects sites for presidio of San Francisco and Mission Dolores on San Francisco Bay.
	May	Leaves San Gabriel Mission to return to Mexico.
	June	Reaches Horcasitas, Sonora, Mexico.
1777		Appointed Governor of New Mexico, but kept in Sonora to put down an Indian uprising.
1778		Goes to New Mexico to assume his new duties. Distinguishes himself for diplomacy in handling Indian troubles.
1783		Accused unjustly of responsibility for the 1781 Yuma massacre.
1786		Removed as Governor of New Mexico.
1788	December	Leaves for Mexico City after his replacement arrives.
		Dies en route. Is buried beneath floor of village church at tiny settlement of Arizpe.

Bibliography

Bancroft, Hubert Howe, *History Of Arizona And New Mexico*, The History Company, San Francisco, California, 1889

Bancroft, Hubert Howe, *History Of California* (Volume I: 1542–1800), A. L. Bancroft & Co., 1884

Bolton, Herbert Eugene, *Anza's California Expeditions* (Volumes I–V, including "Outposts of Empire," and "Translated Diaries of Anza, Garcés and Font"), University of California Press, Berkeley, California, 1930

Caughey, John Walton, *History Of The Pacific Coast*, Prentice-Hall, Inc., New York, 1938

Chapman, Charles E., *History Of California—Spanish Period*, The Macmillan Company, New York, 1926

Cleland, Robert Glass, *California—Pathfinders*, Powell Publishing Co., Los Angeles, California, 1929

Hallenbeck, Cleve, *Land Of The Conquistadores*, Caxton Printers, Ltd., Caldwell, Idaho, 1950

Martin, Douglas D., *Yuma Crossing*, University of New Mexico Press, Albuquerque, New Mexico, 1954

Index